Men's Fi... *magazine*

BUILD A
FIGHTER'S
BODY

by **Joel Snape**

Additional words Ben Ince,
Nick Hutchings, Mark Bailey, Fiaz Rafiq
Art Editor Fanni Williams
Photography Tom Miles, Pete Webb,
Corbis, Getty, Shutterstock
Model Richard P@IMM
Managing Editor Chris Miller
Art Director Donovan Walker

For more information on *Men's Fitness* magazine go to **mensfitness.co.uk**

MAGBOOK

Group Publisher **Russell Blackman**
Group Managing Director **Ian Westwood**
Digital Production Manager **Nicky Baker**
MagBook Publisher **Dharmesh Mistry**
Operations Director **Robin Ryan**
Managing Director of Advertising
Julian Lloyd-Evans
Newstrade Director **David Barker**
Commercial & Retail Director **Martin Belson**
Chief Operating Officer/
Chief Financial Officer **Brett Reynolds**
Group Finance Director **Ian Leggett**
Chief Executive Officer **James Tye**
Chairman **Felix Dennis**

The 'MagBook' brand is a trademark of Dennis Publishing Ltd,
30 Cleveland Street, London W1T 4JD.
Company registered in England.
All material © Dennis Publishing Ltd, licensed by Felden 2012,
and may not be reproduced in whole or part without the
consent of the publishers. Printed in China.

BUILD A FIGHTER'S BODY ISBN 1-78106-036-3
To license this product please contact Nicole Adams on
+44 (0) 20 7907 6134 or email nicole_adams@dennis.co.uk

Advertising
Katie Wood katie_wood@dennis.co.uk
Matt Wakefield matt_wakefield@dennis.co.uk

To subscribe to *Men's Fitness* magazine,
call **0844 844 0081** or go to **mensfitness.co.uk**

CONTENTS

WHAT DRIVES YOU?

PAUL SASS
UFC LIGHTWEIGHT STAR & TEAM PhD ATHLETE

Amino Drive™ is a caffeine free exercise support complex formulated with BCAA'S, L-Glutamine, Tyrosine, DMAE, Vitamin B6, ALC & Choline. Amino Drive™ can be used before or during exercise, or throughout the day to boost amino acid intake. Importantly, Amino Drive™ can be used before evening workouts as it does not contain caffeine, which can disrupt sleep patterns. Available in 2 great tasting PhD flavours.

+ 4g BCAA'S PER SERVING   + 5.5g L-GLUTAMINE & TAURINE

+ CHOLINE, TYROSINE & DMAE   + N-ACETYL L-CARNITINE

+ CAN BE USED PRIOR TO EVENING WORKOUTS

PhD

INNOVATION FOR THE MODERN ATHLETE

www.phd-supplements.com   Find us on: Available at leading retailers   GNC

CHANGE

YOUR VIEW OF MULTIVITAMINS FOREVER

Nexgen® + Sports is a revolutionary multivitamin that is designed specifically for anyone who participates in highly active sport, addressing specific needs that ordinary multivitamins simply fail to meet with its highly sophisticated formulation and unique performance guarantee.

Providing 100% of the athlete's No.1 mineral. Magnesium is absolutely essential for the production of cellular energy and optimal muscle function. Even the smallest deficiency can compromise energy levels, muscle strength and mental focus. Consumption of calcium rich protein sources such as whey protein also results in a greater need for magnesium. Research indicates that the optimal ratio of calcium to magnesium is 2:1. Nexgen® +Sports provides 375mg of magnesium per day from one of the most bioavailable forms available called magnesium citrate, which is significantly more bioavailable than magnesium oxide.

Superior natural vitamin K2 (MK7) and your skeletal structure. Reflex Nexgen® + Sports is one of the only multivitamins in the world to contain super biologically active vitamin K2-MK7, the most expensive form that is used in scientific studies which show its positive effects on VO2 max, muscle cramps, bone health and vascular health. Nexgen® + Sports derives its vitamin K2 MK-7 exclusively from branded superior quality MenaquinGold™.

Vitamin D3 to support a healthy immune system. Vitamin D is not only important for maintaining a healthy bone structure, but also has a role in the immune system, utilisation of magnesium, blood pressure and hormone metabolism. Nexgen® + Sports provides 50µg of pharmaceutical grade vitamin D3, a dose that is very close to what researchers now believe to be better suited for maintaining healthy levels of vitamin D in the body.

Unique antioxidant support. The rigours of exercise and the environment all increase oxidative stress within the body and Nexgen® + Sports contains a wide and varied range of antioxidants in real world dosages and in the highest quality forms; DeltaGold® delta-tocotrienols, Lyc-O-Mato® (natural Lycopene), BIOLUT™ lutein esters, grapeseed extract, green tea extract, Selenium SeLECT® and natural coenzyme Q10.

Additional chelated minerals. Superior quality zinc, copper, manganese, molybdenum and chromium as amino acid chelated minerals. The most expensive form of minerals found in vitamin pills, few products incorporate them exclusively, but Nexgen® + Sports does. These minerals are in chelated form which means that they are minerals which are bonded to amino acids for superior absorption; other brands may use inferior minerals in oxide form like zinc oxide.

Complete vitamin B energy complex including methylcobalamin. Nexgen® + Sports contains a complete high strength vitamin B complex to support a healthy nervous system, release of energy from food and healthy skin & hair. B vitamins are water soluble and the body cannot store them, this is one of the primary reasons that Nexgen® + Sports is taken 3 times a day with meals. Moreover Nexgen® + Sports also contains superior vitamin B12 as methylcobalamin which is the most bioavailable and best utilised form of vitamin B12.

Iron-free formula. Nexgen® + Sports is now iron-free. Today many foods are fortified with iron and therefore it is possible to overdose on it by using further supplementary sources, especially if your diet is rich in foods containing iron.

LactoSpore® probiotics bacillus coagulans. They are very stable compared to other types of probiotics being resistant to stomach acid thereby providing optimal growth in the intestines to benefit intestinal health.

Performance guarantee. Nexgen® + Sports comes with a compelling guarantee; use Nexgen® + Sports as directed and if you are not happy for any reason we will refund you in full. See terms & conditions on our website.

We urge you to visit the science behind the product at:

www.reflex-nutrition.com

 Please visit & join our Facebook page at Reflex Nutrition Ltd

WELCOME

Here's how to get strong, fast and fit like some of the world's best fighters

Joel Snape, editor

On *Men's Fitness* magazine, we meet a lot of professional fighters, and we're always amazed by how hard and how smart they train. Because of the diverse set of skills required by sports such as boxing, Judo and MMA, these athletes are constantly looking for the latest, most effective training techniques. And because almost every fight sport includes weight classes, they keep their lean muscle high and their body fat low, which is a worthwhile aspiration for anyone.

PREPARE FOR COMBAT

Build A Fighter's Body aims to pack all that expertise into one informative and easy-to-use book. In the first section we've put together a 12-week plan

to get you into shape, based on the format of a typical fighter's training camp. Then, once you're in shape, you can tweak your training with moves, routines and tricks from top-level athletes and coaches. There's also advice on how to tailor your diet to your new training plan, and how to improve your recovery – which is just as vital as training hard. Whether you want to fight or you're after a fighter's body, there's something for you inside.

The workouts in this book were shot at Stars Gym, one of London's leading martial arts and fitness facilities. Stars offers classes for all abilities, in an uplifting gym environment. For more visit starsgym.co.uk

STARSGYM

FIGHT TRAINING FAQ

No-nonsense answers to your fight fitness questions

Q How should I use this book?
You've got a few options. If you want a comprehensive plan for getting in fight shape fast, you should follow the Fight Camp plan that starts on p16. This is a 12-week programme that starts by giving you a good base of strength and then builds on it with conditioning and endurance workouts. If you're looking for a challenge or way to work on certain aspects of your fitness, you'll find workout plans and tips from a variety of MMA fighters, boxers and coaches in the second half of the book.

Q Can I combine these plans with other training?
That's how they're designed. Fighters can't afford to hit the gym every day on top of their sport-specific training, so they make their training as efficient as possible by using compound, multi-joint movements and exercising their entire body every time they train. If you want to work on your boxing, play five-a-side or go for a run between these workouts, that's fine – just make sure you're getting plenty of protein and sleep to maximise your recovery.

Q Can I use machines instead of free weights?
Resistance machines have their place in the gym: they're a great way for beginners to build a base level of strength without risk of injury, and they can let experienced gym-goers isolate muscles. But because they restrict movement, they don't recruit the stabilising muscles that are vital for success in combat sports, and can force you to move unnaturally. Focus on perfect form with free weights and you'll get great results.

▶

Q *How long should these workouts take?*

Ideally, your workout should take less than an hour. Research suggests that levels of the growth hormone testosterone peak around 45 minutes into a workout and then quickly subside as levels of cortisol, the stress hormone that breaks down muscle tissue and damages cells, rise. So keep your workouts short to keep them effective.

Q *Will training this way give me a six-pack?*

It certainly can. Every one of these workouts includes plenty of abs work, whether it comes from direct moves like sit-ups or core twists, or from using the abs as stabilisers in big moves like the squat. But it doesn't matter how much you build up your abs if they're still hidden under a layer of fat, which is why trainers are fond of saying that abs are built in the kitchen. That's why we've included a comprehensive guide to eating to maximise muscle growth, fat loss and recovery starting on p170.

Q *How quickly can I expect results?*

Even with the help of this book, don't expect overnight success. You need to regularly lift heavy weights to stimulate your muscles into growth, eat a clean diet and get plenty of sleep. On the plus side, if you focus on improving the reps and weights you can handle in the gym, you'll be amazed by the changes in your body shape.

Q *Do I actually need to fight anybody?*

Nope. Fighting might have other benefits, including helping your self-confidence, co-ordination and stress levels, but if you really don't want to get punched or armlocked, actual fighting isn't a part of this plan.

FITNESS TIP
If you're unsure about your ability to handle any aspect of this training, it's worth checking with your GP first.

FIGHT CAMP

Whether you're preparing for a fight or not,
our 12-week plan will build muscle, strip fat
and get you in the best shape of your life

YOUR FIGHT PLAN

How to go from couch to cage in just 12 weeks

The aim of this plan is simple: to get you in fight shape as quickly as possible. Fighters need to be strong, fast, explosive and well conditioned, while maintaining a low body fat percentage, so they're some of the world's best all-round athletes. This plan has been designed to get you into that sort of shape by Grapplefit's Barry Gibson, a strength and conditioning coach who's been involved in judo, Sambo and wrestling for over a decade. Like many fighters' programmes, it involves three sessions a week – two focused on strength and one conditioning workout. If you're training for a fight, or just to improve your fight-specific strength, it's designed to mesh with your current schedule. If you just want to get in fighting shape, it'll do that too.

HOW IT WORKS

The workouts are designed to mimic a professional fighter's training camp, which typically lasts from eight to 12 weeks. In the first phase you'll build strength with big movements and simple bodyweight exercises. Then you move on to applying that strength with power-based moves, building your strength-endurance with higher-rep sets.

WORKOUT FREQUENCY

It's fine to combine this plan with technique or sparring sessions, extra cardio or other sports. On the other hand, focus on these workouts should make your progress faster. It's a good idea to have a rest day between workouts if you can, though.

FIGHTING WEIGHT

Pick a weight that means you struggle to complete the last couple of reps of each set. This will vary across the moves, so use your warm-up sets to work out what weight you think you can manage. It's better to go light in the first week of each month and then push yourself later than risk injury.

SOUND NUTRITION

You don't need to follow a restrictive diet. Eat fresh food, get plenty of protein, and avoid refined carbohydrates such as white bread. You'll find the nutrition rules you should live by on p170.

THE COACH
Barry Gibson has more than 20 years' experience training and competing in martial arts, including fighting on a national level in judo and Sambo. He trains fighters including the UFC's Ross Pearson under his own system, Grapplefit. Find out more at grapplefit.com

---

WORKOUT THEORY *Each routine is shown in table form. Here's how they break down*

WEEK
Four weeks isn't long enough for your body to get used to the exercises so that it stops responding. This means you can do the same moves each week and get results, particularly if you vary sets, reps or weight. If the rep count goes down in a workout, this means you should go heavier.

REPS
This is the number of times you perform an exercise in each set. In the strength workouts use a low rep count to help you get stronger without adding unnecessary bulk. In the conditioning workouts, you'll do higher reps to work on strength endurance or cardio.

SETS
In general, the number of sets increases as the programme goes on and you get used to the moves. On big moves such as the deadlift and push press, do a few warm-up sets with an empty bar and gradually increase the weight to prime your body before you start your work sets.

REST
When you do supersets aim to take no rest between exercises, then rest for the allotted time between circuits. In the strength workouts, you get long rests to allow you to recover between sets. In the conditioning ones, they're timed to mimic the break between rounds in a fight.

BUILDING STRONG FOUNDATIONS

Whatever your fitness goals, building a solid base of strength is crucial. If you want to lose fat or build muscle it'll let you shift bigger weights to improve your gym gains, and if you want to fight it'll allow you to manhandle an opponent more effectively. Hit the weights hard in month one and you'll reap the benefits later.

How to do the workouts
Get strong and add muscle with your first four weeks of training

Each of the programmes in this chapter is based on doing three sessions a week: two aimed at building strength and one focused on conditioning. This mimics how many fighters structure their routines – they get a lot of endurance work from sports-specific training, so they use their time in the gym to get stronger, while keeping one session a week to really push their cardio.

For the first month your strength sessions are full-body workouts focusing on big, multi-joint moves that will teach you to move your body as a unit. If you're new to lifting, spend a couple of weeks familiarising yourself with the moves and working on technique – this will help in the long run. If you're an experienced gym-goer, go for the biggest weights you can manage with proper form.

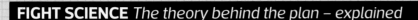

FIGHT SCIENCE *The theory behind the plan – explained*

Moves such as the deadlift, squat and push press involve several of the body's larger muscle groups. This means that not only are they an efficient way to work out, but they'll prompt the release of growth hormone and testosterone, helping your muscle gains.

In exercise science, intensity refers to how close the weight you're lifting is to your one-rep max. For your big moves you should lift at a relatively high intensity – 80% or over – which should lead to rapid strength gains. When the reps get lower, increase the weight.

The volume of lifting you're doing refers to how many reps you do in total. This programme is relatively low-volume compared with more bodybuilding-specific plans, which means muscle soreness will be kept to a minimum so you're fresh for your other training sessions.

STRENGTH WORKOUT 1

This workout starts with a big full-body move to get every muscle group involved and increase your testosterone levels. It follows up with a mixture of pushing and pulling moves using your entire body, including some unilateral moves to keep your body in balance. It finishes with a burst of conditioning to keep you burning fat throughout the day.

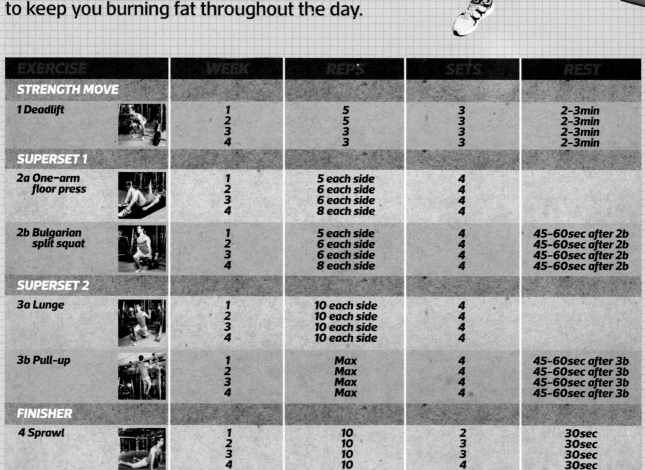

EXERCISE		WEEK	REPS	SETS	REST
STRENGTH MOVE					
1 Deadlift		1	5	3	2–3min
		2	5	3	2–3min
		3	3	3	2–3min
		4	3	3	2–3min
SUPERSET 1					
2a One-arm floor press		1	5 each side	4	
		2	6 each side	4	
		3	6 each side	4	
		4	8 each side	4	
2b Bulgarian split squat		1	5 each side	4	45–60sec after 2b
		2	6 each side	4	45–60sec after 2b
		3	6 each side	4	45–60sec after 2b
		4	8 each side	4	45–60sec after 2b
SUPERSET 2					
3a Lunge		1	10 each side	4	
		2	10 each side	4	
		3	10 each side	4	
		4	10 each side	4	
3b Pull-up		1	Max	4	45–60sec after 3b
		2	Max	4	45–60sec after 3b
		3	Max	4	45–60sec after 3b
		4	Max	4	45–60sec after 3b
FINISHER					
4 Sprawl		1	10	2	30sec
		2	10	3	30sec
		3	10	3	30sec
		4	10	4	30sec

1 Deadlift
Targets Total body

WHY DO IT

This full-body move is one of the best strength-builders around, working your lower back, grip and legs and letting you shift serious amounts of weight.

HOW TO DO IT

Grip the bar just outside your knees with your core braced and your shoulders retracted and over the bar. Your back should be flat and your shins should be close to the bar. If you're lifting heavy, use an alternate grip (pictured).

Push through your heels to lift the bar, keeping your chest up and driving your hips forward as the bar passes your knees.

2a One-arm floor press
Targets Chest, triceps

WHY DO IT

Unilateral pushing is useful for everything from punching to BJJ, and also forces you to stabilise your core as you press.

HOW TO DO IT

Lie with a dumbbell or kettlebell in one hand, holding it up with your elbow bent at 90° and your forearm vertical.

Press the dumbbell overhead, then lower it under control. Finish all your reps on one side before changing hands.

2b Bulgarian split squat
Targets Hamstrings, glutes, quads

WHY DO IT

- It's a great move for unilateral leg strength. As an added bonus doing it with dumbbells will test your grip.

HOW TO DO IT

- Hold a dumbbell in each hand and rest one foot on a bench, instep down.
- Squat down with your leading leg until your trailing knee almost touches the floor, then drive back up.
- Finish all your reps on one side before switching legs.

a

b

3a Lunge
Targets Hamstrings, glutes, quads

WHY DO IT

- Unilateral leg strength is very important for a fighter, whether you're driving forward for a takedown or balancing yourself during a kick.

HOW TO DO IT

- Hold a bar across your shoulders, with your hands slightly wider than shoulder-width apart.
- Take a large step forward with one leg. The knee of your back leg should brush the floor, and your front knee shouldn't move beyond your toes.
- Return to the standing position, then repeat the move on the other leg.

a

b

3b Pull-up
Targets Upper back, core

WHY DO IT

- It builds a strong back, balances out the 'pushing' you do in fighting, and is surprisingly tough on your core.

HOW TO DO IT

- Grasp the bar with an overhand grip. The wider apart your hands are, the harder the move becomes.
- Start from a dead hang with your arms fully extended.
- Pull yourself up until your chin is over the bar, then lower yourself back to the start position.

4 Sprawl
Targets

WHY DO IT

- It's a close cousin of the burpee and is also a fundamental move in fighting, teaching you to get your legs back and hips down in order to stop a takedown.

HOW TO DO IT

- Start in a fighting stance. You can keep your hands high, like a boxer, or low, which is the position you'd take if you were anticipating a wrestling shot.
- Kick your legs backwards and drop your hips to the mat. Support your weight on your hands and keep your chest up.

STRENGTH WORKOUT 2

This workout starts with a big move that will teach your body to move as a unit, then follows up with a pair of antagonistic supersets to give you a full-body workout including pulling, pushing and squatting. Finally, you'll hit some burpees to get you used to level changes and start working on a solid base of conditioning.

EXERCISE		WEEK	REPS	SETS	REST
STRENGTH MOVE					
1 Push press		1	8	3	2–3min
		2	8	3	2–3min
		3	6	3	2–3min
		4	6	3	2–3min
SUPERSET 1					
2a Back squat		1	6	4	
		2	6	4	
		3	8	4	
		4	8	4	
2b Shoulder press		1	6	4	45–60sec after 2b
		2	6	4	45–60sec after 2b
		3	8	4	45–60sec after 2b
		4	8	4	45–60sec after 2b
SUPERSET 2					
3a Chin-up		1	6	4	
		2	8	4	
		3	8	4	
		4	10	4	
3b Diamond press-up		1	10	4	45–60sec after 3b
		2	12	4	45–60sec after 3b
		3	12	4	45–60sec after 3b
		4	15	4	45–60sec after 3b
FINISHER					
4 Burpee		1	10	2	30sec
		2	10	3	30sec
		3	10	3	30sec
		4	10	4	30sec

1 Push press
Targets Shoulders, triceps

WHY DO IT

- Using your legs to assist the move allows you to lift heavier, involving your whole body and priming your muscles for growth.

HOW TO DO IT

- **Stand with your feet shoulder-width apart, holding a bar with your hands in a comfortable position.**
- **Perform a quarter-squat, then use the momentum as you come up to forcefully drive the bar upwards.**
- **Lower the bar under control.**

a

b

2a Back squat
Targets Glutes, hamstrings, quads

WHY DO IT

- It's a great all-round strength builder, which also triggers testosterone and growth hormone to make you bigger.

HOW TO DO IT

- **Rest the bar across the back of your shoulders – you might find that squeezing it helps you stabilise your upper body. Keep your feet shoulder-width apart, and slightly turned out.**
- **Squat back and down as if you're sitting on a chair. At the bottom of the move, your thighs should be parallel to the floor. Keep your chest up.**
- **Drive up through your heels, keeping your chest up.**

a

b

2b Shoulder press
Targets

WHY DO IT

- It's a great shoulder-builder and a surprisingly challenging test of core strength.

HOW TO DO IT

- Hold a bar across the top of your chest with your hands slightly more than shoulder-width apart. Your forearms should be vertical.

- Press the bar upwards without moving your legs. You'll create a stronger base if you squeeze your glutes and brace your abs, which will allow you to press more weight.

3a Chin-up
Targets

WHY DO IT

- It builds a strong back, but increases the biceps involvement compared with an overhand pull-up.

HOW TO DO IT

- Grasp the bar with an underhand grip, with your hands roughly shoulder-width apart.

- Start from a dead hang with your arms fully extended.

- Pull yourself up until your chin is over the bar, then lower yourself back to the start position.

3b Diamond press-up
Targets Triceps, chest

WHY DO IT

O Having your hands close together shifts the focus away from the chest and towards your triceps.

HOW TO DO IT

O Start in a press-up position but with your hands close together so that opposite thumbs and index fingers touch to form a diamond.

O Keeping your body in a straight line from head to heels, lower your chest to the ground, then press back up strongly to the start position.

a

b

4 Burpee
Targets Total body

WHY DO IT

O It works multiple muscle groups at once and gets your heart rate soaring.

HOW TO DO IT

O Start standing with your arms fully extended above your head, then squat down.

O As you reach the bottom of the squat, put your hands down and kick your legs back, landing in a press-up position.

O Perform a press-up, then bring your legs back underneath you and jump up off the ground.

a

b

c

CONDITIONING WORKOUT 1

For the first four weeks of your conditioning plan, you'll do a circuit of simple bodyweight exercises. You're going by time rather than reps, so how hard you push yourself is up to you – but the harder you work, the better your results will be.

HOW TO DO THE WORKOUT

- Below is a five-minute 'round', broken into 30-second chunks of bodyweight moves.
- Do each exercise as hard and as fast as possible.
- As the weeks progress you'll increase the number of rounds, until you're working hard for the equivalent of a five-round title fight.
- Try to hit as many reps as possible, and better your score with each round if you can.

EXERCISE	TIME
Burpee	30 seconds
Press-up	30 seconds
Divebomber press-up	30 seconds
Mountain climber	30 seconds
Sprawl	30 seconds
Squat thrust	30 seconds
Press-up	30 seconds
Divebomber press-up	30 seconds
Mountain climber	30 seconds
Sprawl	30 seconds

WEEK	ROUNDS	REST
1	2	45sec
2	3	45sec
3	4	60sec
4	5	60sec

If you need to rest, try to rest in the top position of the move rather than sitting or lying down, so you get a breather while still working your muscles.

1 Burpee
Targets **Total body**

WHY DO IT

○ It's a great move for working multiple muscle groups at once and getting your heart rate soaring.

HOW TO DO IT

○ **Start in a standing position, then squat down.**

○ **As you reach the bottom of the squat, put your hands down and kick your legs back, landing in a press-up position.**

○ **Perform a press-up, then bring your legs back underneath you and jump up off the ground.**

2 Press-up
Targets **Chest, triceps**

WHY DO IT

○ It's the classic chest-builder and demands a fair amount of core strength.

HOW TO DO IT

○ **Hold your body in a straight line with your hands roughly underneath your shoulders.**

○ **Lower yourself until your chest touches the floor, then push back up until your arms are straight.**

3 Divebomber press-up
Targets **Chest, shoulders**

WHY DO IT

○ It's a twist on the traditional press-up that works the muscles from different angles, as well as working the flexibility of your hamstrings and lower back.

HOW TO DO IT

○ Start with your hands and feet slightly closer together than in a traditional press-up, so that you're almost in an inverted V.

○ Bend your arms and lower your chest almost to the floor, then bring it up at the end of the move.

○ Reverse the move to return to the start position.

4 Mountain climber
Targets **Glutes, hamstrings, core**

WHY DO IT

○ It's a tough conditioning move, with the added bonus that it'll work your dynamic flexibility.

HOW TO DO IT

○ Starting from a press-up position, jump one foot forward so that it lands close to your hands. Keep your hips down.

○ Jump and switch positions with your feet, the other one landing forward.

5 Squat thrust
Targets Glutes, hamstrings

WHY DO IT

- It's a classic conditioning move – low-skill, easy to do, and an absolute lung-scorcher.

HOW TO DO IT

- Start in a press-up position. Jump your feet forward until they're as close to your hands as possible, then jump them back out again.

6 Sprawl
Targets Total body

WHY DO IT

- It's a close cousin of the burpee that's also a fundamental move in fighting, teaching you to get your legs back and hips down in order to stop a takedown.

HOW TO DO IT

- Start in a fighting stance. You can keep your hands high, like a boxer, or low, which is the position you'd take if you were anticipating a wrestling shot.

- Kick your legs backwards and drop your hips to the mat. Support your weight on your hands and keep your chest up.

DAVID PRICE
Lonsdale Ambassador
British & Commonwealth Heavyweight Champion

WIN
THE ULTIMATE FIGHT SPORTS STARTER KIT

FIRMLY ESTABLISHED AS THE LEADING BRAND OF FITNESS AND FIGHT SPORTS EQUIPMENT AND CLOTHING, LONSDALE IS STEEPED IN OVER 50 YEARS OF FIGHT SPORTS HISTORY

From humble London origins the Lonsdale brand quickly became a hallmark of both boxing and MMA champions throughout the world, with its legendary quality and authenticity. It's no coincidence that legends such as Muhammad Ali, Henry Cooper, Joe Calzaghe, Ricky Hatton, Carl Froch and David Price have all trained and fought in Lonsdale.

Celebrities such as Paul Weller, Jason Statham, JLS, The Saturdays, Amy Childs plus many more have chosen to wear Lonsdale clothing. It's the combination of boxing heritage with British culture and an iconic style which makes Lonsdale a true champion both in and out of the ring.

This is your chance to be kitted out like a true Lonsdale champion. Just send your name and contact details via email to Lonsdale@mensfitness.co.uk.

£350 WORTH OF KIT INCLUDING:

PRO TRAINING GLOVES,
4FT HEAVY PUNCHBAG, SWIFT BOXING BOOTS,
SPORTS HOLDALL, T-SHIRT,
CLASSIC LONSDALE HOODY,
TRAINING SHORTS, BASEBALL CAP
PLUS MUCH MORE...

Winners will be contacted after the closing date, 31st May 2013.
Competition terms and conditions can be found at www.mensfitness.co.uk.

FOR ALL THE LATEST NEWS & INFORMATION VISIT
FACEBOOK.COM/LONSDALE OR TWITTER @LONSDALE1960

LONSDALE
LONDON

WWW.LONSDALE.COM

POWERING UP

Now that you've got a solid foundation of strength, it's time to work on your power. For fighters, it's no use being able to bench huge numbers if you can't throw a punch quickly, and a double-bodyweight deadlift isn't very helpful if you haven't got the speed to hit a takedown. The next four weeks will help you take your gym strength into the ring.

How to do the workouts
Get explosive with these power-centric training plans

For your second month of fight camp, you'll be working opposing muscle groups to push your strength endurance and doing plyometric moves to build power. Once again, you'll be doing three sessions a week for a total of four weeks, and again, you should stick to using weights you can handle with proper form. If you're going to really push yourself, do it on the bodyweight moves – aiming to be as explosive as possible in these will help you transfer your gym gains to your fight training.

You should also be going as hard as you can during the conditioning workouts. By the end of this month, you'll be doing five rounds of nonstop movement. And remember: even if you've got no intention of getting in a cage, challenging your muscles with different types of movement will shock them into growth and provide big gains.

FIGHT SCIENCE *The theory behind the plan – explained*

SUPERSETS
Month one's workouts included supersets – back-to-back sets of different exercises – but they're increasingly important for the next four weeks. Antagonistic supersets, which pair moves that work opposing muscle groups (eg bench press and bent-over row), should allow you to lift more weight by activating the stabiliser muscles for each move, as well as keeping your body in balance.

UNILATERAL MOVEMENTS
This refers to any movement in which you focus on one side of the body. They're vital for sports, as you'll rarely drive off both legs at the same time, and will also help to balance out your training.

ISOMETRICS
Moves such as the plank are isometric, which means that they're done in a static position. This is helpful for fighters, who often need to hold grappling positions, but will also help shock your muscles into growth.

STRENGTH WORKOUT 3

This workout starts with a squat variation that's ideal for fight strength, and follows up with a push–pull workout to tax your entire body. Finally, you'll do as many inverted rows as you can for a test of core strength and grip. Record your cumulative totals in the two 'max' exercises – you should be aiming to improve them every week.

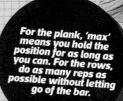

For the plank, 'max' means you hold the position for as long as you can. For the rows, do as many reps as possible without letting go of the bar.

EXERCISE		WEEK	REPS	SETS	REST
STRENGTH MOVE					
1 Zercher squat		1	5	5	90sec–2min
		2	5	5	90sec–2min
		3	5	5	90sec–2min
		4	5	5	90sec–2min
SUPERSET 1					
2a Bench press		1	6	4	
		2	6	4	
		3	8	4	
		4	8	4	
2b Bent-over row		1	6	4	45–60sec after 2b
		2	6	4	45–60sec after 2b
		3	8	4	45–60sec after 2b
		4	8	4	45–60sec after 2b
SUPERSET 2					
3a Reverse curl		1	10	2	
		2	10	2	
		3	10	2	
		4	10	2	
3b Plank hold		1	Max	2	45–60sec after 3b
		2	Max	2	45–60sec after 3b
		3	Max	2	45–60sec after 3b
		4	Max	2	45–60sec after 3b
FINISHER					
4 Inverted row		1	Max	3	45–60sec
		2	Max	3	45–60sec
		3	Max	4	45–60sec
		4	Max	4	45–60sec

1 Zercher squat
Targets Glutes, core, biceps

WHY DO IT
- It's a great core builder, with the added bonus that it mimics the sort of positions you'll get in while fighting for a takedown from a wrestling clinch.

HOW TO DO IT
- Hold a bar in the crook of your elbows with feet shoulder-width apart.
- Squat until your thighs are horizontal, then drive up through your heels.

2a Bench press
Targets Chest, triceps

WHY DO IT
- This classic lift lets you shift more weight than any other upper-body move, making it a favourite for those who want a strong torso, chest and shoulders.

HOW TO DO IT
- Lie on a bench with your feet on the floor, gripping a bar slightly wider than shoulder-width apart.
- Lower the bar to your chest, pause, then drive it back up again. At the bottom of the move, your forearms should be vertical and your upper arms should be at a 45° angle to your torso.

2b Bent-over row
Targets **Upper back, biceps**

WHY DO IT

- It's one of the heaviest horizontal pulling moves you can do, balancing out the muscles you're working in the bench press and giving you a powerful back.

HOW TO DO IT

- **Start with your core braced, your back straight and shoulder blades retracted.**
- **Bend your knees slightly and lean forward from the hips.**
- **Grip the bar with your hands just wider than shoulder-width apart.**
- **Pull the bar up to your lower abs, retracting your shoulder blades, then lower it under control.**

3a Reverse barbell curl
Targets **Biceps, grip**

WHY DO IT

- It's got the same benefits as the classic biceps curl and will also test your grip and forearm strength.

HOW TO DO IT

- **Stand tall with your shoulders back and feet close together, holding a barbell with your hands shoulder-width apart.**
- **Keeping your elbows close to your sides, curl the barbell up to shoulder height. Return the weight to the starting position.**

3b Plank
Targets Core

WHY DO IT

- It works your core muscles to build a strong link between your upper and lower body.

HOW TO DO IT

- Hold your body in a straight line from your head to your heels. You can rest on your elbows to make the move easier, but this variation will improve your press-up numbers.

- Hold the position for as long as you can without letting your hips sag.

4 Inverted row
Targets Upper back, grip

WHY DO IT

- It's a full-body pulling move, working your core stability at the same time as testing your grip and back muscles.

HOW TO DO IT

- Hang from a bar with your body in a straight line and your feet on the floor.

- Pull up until your chest touches the bar, then lower yourself under control.

STRENGTH WORKOUT 4

This workout is designed to enhance explosive strength. The first move in each pair is strength-based and will activate and fire up the neuromuscular system. Then you'll do an explosive movement following a similar pattern of motion. With the muscle fibres activated, you'll get more activation during the second part of the drill.

'Sub max' means you shouldn't go to failure on the sets of pull-ups. Stop when you feel like you could still manage another couple of reps.

EXERCISE		WEEK	REPS	SETS	REST
SUPERSET 1					
1a Back squat		1	8	3	
		2	8	3	
		3	6	4	
		4	6	4	
1b Jump squat		1	10	3	90sec after 1b
		2	10	3	90sec after 1b
		3	10	4	60sec after 1b
		4	10	4	60sec after 1b
SUPERSET 2					
2a One-arm floor press		1	8 each side	3	
		2	8 each side	3	
		3	8 each side	4	
		4	8 each side	4	
2b Clap press-up		1	10	3	90sec after 2b
		2	10	3	90sec after 2b
		3	10	4	60sec after 2b
		4	10	4	60sec after 2b
SUPERSET 3					
3a Pull-up		1	Sub max	4	
		2	Sub max	4	
		3	Sub max	4	
		4	Sub max	4	
3b Medicine ball slam		1	6	4	90sec after 3b
		2	6	4	90sec after 3b
		3	6	4	90sec after 3b
		4	6	4	90sec after 3b

1a Back squat
Targets Glutes, hamstrings

WHY DO IT

- It's a great all-round strength builder, which also triggers testosterone and growth hormone to make you bigger.

HOW TO DO IT

- Rest the bar across the back of your shoulders – you might find that squeezing it helps you stabilise your upper body. Keep your feet shoulder-width apart, and slightly turned out.

- Squat back and down as if you're sitting on a chair. At the bottom of the move, your thighs should be parallel to the floor. Keep your chest up.

- Drive up through your heels, keeping your chest up.

a

b

1b Jump squat
Targets Glutes

WHY DO IT

- It's a great move for explosiveness and also works as a warm-up for weighted squats by getting your fast-twitch muscle fibres firing.

HOW TO DO IT

- Start with your feet shoulder-width apart and your arms in a comfortable position.

- Squat down, then explode upwards, aiming to get as much height as you can.

- Reset between reps, so that you can be as explosive as possible in each one.

a

b

c

2a One-arm floor press
Targets Triceps, chest

WHY DO IT

- Unilateral pushing is useful for everything from punching to BJJ, and also forces you to stabilise your core as you press.

HOW TO DO IT

- Lie with a dumbbell or kettlebell in one hand, holding it up with your elbow bent at 90° and your forearm vertical.

- Press the dumbbell overhead, then lower it under control. Finish all your reps on one side before changing hands.

a

b

2b Clap press-up
Targets Triceps, chest

WHY DO IT

- Clapping between press-ups means you have to push explosively, turning this into a plyometric move ideal for building punching power.

HOW TO DO IT

- Start in a press-up position and lower your chest to the ground.

- Press back up powerfully so that your hands leave the floor. Quickly clap, then land and descend into the next rep.

a

b

c

3a Pull-up
Targets **Back, core**

WHY DO IT

○ It builds a strong back, balances out the 'pushing' you do in fighting, and is surprisingly tough on your core.

HOW TO DO IT

○ Grasp the bar with an overhand grip. The wider apart your hands are, the harder the move becomes.

○ Start from a dead hang with your arms fully extended.

○ Pull yourself up until your chin is over the bar, then lower yourself back to the start position.

3b Medicine ball slam
Targets **Back, core**

WHY DO IT

○ It's an explosive move in which you don't need to decelerate, because you're letting go of the weight at the bottom.

HOW TO DO IT

○ Hold a medicine ball in both hands, bring it behind your head and slam it to the floor as hard as possible.

○ If you're focusing on cardio, retrieve the ball as fast as possible. If you're working on explosiveness, reset between reps for maximum power.

CONDITIONING WORKOUT 2

For your second month of fight conditioning, you'll do a series of full-body moves. There's a lot of going from standing to the floor, which mimics the scrambles that happen in a real-life fight – and also puts your body to the test.

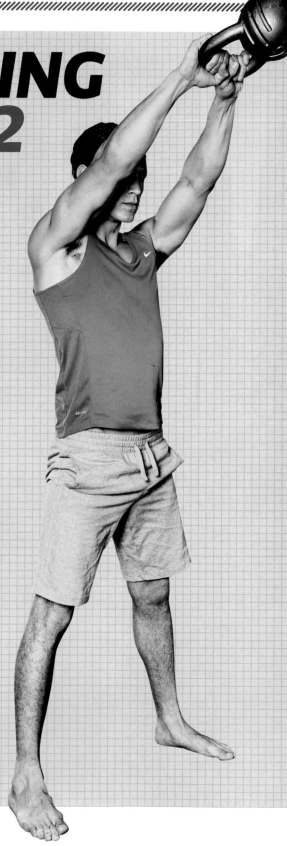

HOW TO DO THE WORKOUT

- Do each move in turn, getting through the 'rounds' as fast as possible. You'll do more rounds, with less rest, as the weeks go by.
- If you really want to put yourself to the test, do a 20m shuttle run between each exercise.

EXERCISE	REPS
Truck jump	10
Mountain climber	20
Burpee	10
Squat thrust	10
Spider-Man press-up	10
Kettlebell swing	10

WEEK	ROUNDS	REST
1	3	60sec
2	4	60sec
3	4	45sec
4	5	45sec

1 Tuck jump
Targets Glutes, hamstrings

WHY DO IT

○ It's an explosive move that's great for building impressive cardio.

HOW TO DO IT

○ Perform a quarter–squat, then jump as high as possible, tucking your knees towards your chest at the top of the move.

2 Mountain climber
Targets Glutes, hamstrings, core

WHY DO IT

○ It's a tough conditioning move, with the added bonus that it'll work your dynamic flexibility.

HOW TO DO IT

○ Starting from a press–up position, jump one foot forward so that it lands close to your hands. Keep your hips down.

○ Jump and switch positions with your feet, the other one landing forward.

3 Burpee
Targets **Total body**

WHY DO IT

- It's a great move for working multiple muscle groups at once and getting your heart rate soaring.

HOW TO DO IT

- Start standing with your arms fully extended above your head, then squat down.

- As you reach the bottom of the squat, put your hands down and kick your legs back, landing in a press-up position.

- Perform a press-up, then bring your legs back underneath you and jump up off the ground.

a

b

c

4 Squat thrust
Targets **Glutes, hamstrings**

WHY DO IT

- It's a classic conditioning move – low-skill, easy to do, and an absolute lung-scorcher.

HOW TO DO IT

- Start in a press-up position. Jump your feet forward until they're as close to your hands as possible, then jump them back out again.

a

b

5 Spider-Man press-up
Targets Chest, core

WHY DO IT

○ It's a version of the press-up that tests your core strength and balance, as well as working on your hip mobility.

HOW TO DO IT

○ Start at the top of a press-up position.

○ As you lower yourself to the floor, bring one knee up and to the side until it's as close as possible to your elbow. Repeat on the other side.

6 Kettlebell swing
Targets Glutes, hamstrings

WHY DO IT

○ It's an explosive move that works your whole posterior chain, as well as giving you a great cardio hit. If you haven't got a kettlebell, grip a dumbbell by its end.

HOW TO DO IT

○ Stand holding a kettlebell, with your feet just wider than shoulder-width apart, slightly pointed outwards.

○ Lower yourself as if you're sitting on a chair, letting the kettlebell swing between your legs.

○ Contract your glutes forcefully as you 'pop' your hips forward. You should be able to see underneath the kettlebell at the top of its swing.

GOING THE DISTANCE

It's the final month of fight camp, and by now you should be a strong, explosive mass of lean, fast-twitch muscle. You'll have built up a decent base of strength endurance and cardio from your conditioning workouts, but now it's time to step things up. Upping the reps and decreasing the rest periods will shift any remaining body fat and leave you ripped and ready for anything.

How to do the workouts
Get ring-ready with your last month of training

For the last four weeks of fight camp, you'll be doing less high-intensity strength work and more high-rep moves. This mimics the sort of training fighters do in the last few weeks before a bout, when they'll be aiming to build the conditioning to fight hard in every round if necessary. Another benefit of these sorts of workouts is that they'll ramp up your metabolism for hours afterwards

– handy whether you need to weigh in for a fight or just burn some excess fat.

Don't worry if you can't handle as much weight on the bar as you've used in the previous months of the plan, but it's worth making every effort to be strict about your rest periods. This is what's going to give you the most benefits, and nobody's going to give you an extra ten seconds to breathe in the ring.

FIGHT SCIENCE *The theory behind the plan – explained*

PLYOMETRICS
These are exercises designed to produce fast and powerful movements, by allowing the muscles to exert maximum force in the shortest time possible. The term is commonly associated with jumping movements but can also refer to moves in which you throw something explosively.

COMPLEXES
One of the strength workouts this month involves a barbell complex – several different exercises during which you don't put the bar down. This will test your grip and cardio, but also give you a serious fat-burning, muscle-building jolt thanks to the time your muscles spend under tension.

GRIP WORK
Between rope slams and sledgehammer swings, this month heavily emphasises your grip. That's important because your grip can limit you in workouts if it isn't strong enough. The more grip endurance and strength you have, the more weight you'll be able to shift and the more control you can exert over an opponent.

STRENGTH WORKOUT 5

Now that you've built up a decent base of strength, it's time to make sure you can go the distance. Tackle this strength-endurance complex with slightly less weight than you did for the lower-rep, longer-rest sets in the first two months, but make sure that you're still using a weight that makes it challenge to get through all the reps. Do every exercise, then rest and repeat the circuit.

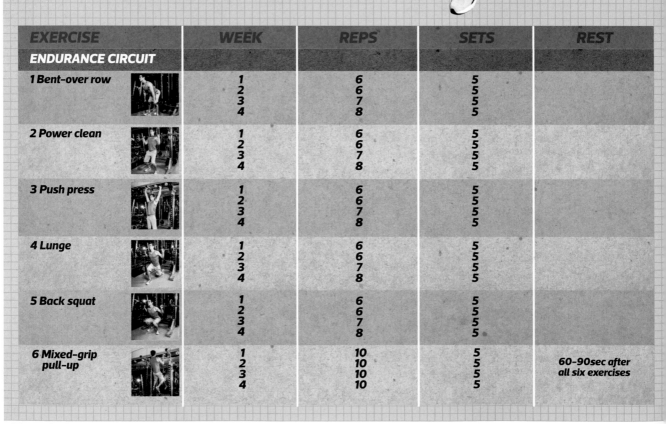

EXERCISE	WEEK	REPS	SETS	REST
ENDURANCE CIRCUIT				
1 Bent-over row	1 2 3 4	6 6 7 8	5 5 5 5	
2 Power clean	1 2 3 4	6 6 7 8	5 5 5 5	
3 Push press	1 2 3 4	6 6 7 8	5 5 5 5	
4 Lunge	1 2 3 4	6 6 7 8	5 5 5 5	
5 Back squat	1 2 3 4	6 6 7 8	5 5 5 5	
6 Mixed-grip pull-up	1 2 3 4	10 10 10 10	5 5 5 5	*60–90sec after all six exercises*

1 Bent-over row
Targets **Upper back, biceps**

WHY DO IT

- It's one of the heaviest horizontal pulling moves you can do, balancing out the muscles you're working in the bench press and giving you a powerful back.

HOW TO DO IT

- **Start with your core braced, your back straight and shoulder blades retracted.**
- **Bend your knees slightly and lean forward from the hips.**
- **Grip the bar with your arms just wider than shoulder-width apart.**
- **Pull the bar up to your lower abs, retracting your shoulder blades, then lower it under control.**

2 Power clean
Targets **Total body**

WHY DO IT

- It's one of the heaviest horizontal pulling moves you can do, balancing out the muscles you're working in the bench press and giving you a powerful back.

HOW TO DO IT

- **The clean involves almost all your major muscle groups and forces them to work together to generate explosive power.**
- **Lift the bar off the ground by driving up through your heels.**
- **Once the bar reaches your hips, rise up on tiptoes, shrug your shoulders and pull the bar up to the front of your shoulders.**

3 Push press
Targets Total body

WHY DO IT

- It's a full-body move that works your explosiveness and co-ordination.

HOW TO DO IT

- Hold a bar across the top of your chest with your hands slightly wider than shoulder-width apart. Your forearms should be vertical.

- Perform a quarter-squat, then as you come up, use your momentum to help drive the bar overhead.

4 Lunge
Targets Glutes, hamstrings

WHY DO IT

- Unilateral leg strength is very important for a fighter, whether you're driving forward for a takedown or balancing yourself during a kick.

HOW TO DO IT

- Hold a bar across your shoulders, with your hands slightly wider than shoulder-width apart.

- Take a large step forward with one leg. The knee of your rear leg should brush the floor, and your front knee shouldn't move beyond your toes.

- Return to the standing position, then repeat the move on the other leg.

5 Back squat
Targets Glutes, quads, hamstrings

WHY DO IT

- It's a great all-round strength builder that also triggers testosterone and growth hormone to make you bigger.

HOW TO DO IT

- Rest the bar across the back of your shoulders – you might find that squeezing it helps you stabilise your upper body. Keep your feet shoulder-width apart, and slightly turned out.
- Squat back and down as if you're sitting on a chair. At the bottom of the move, your thighs should be parallel to the floor. Keep your chest up.
- Drive up through your heels, keeping your chest up.

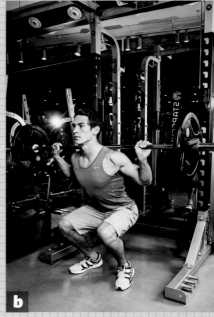

6 Mixed-grip pull-up
Targets Back, grip

WHY DO IT

- It's a challenging twist on the traditional pull-up, and mimics the awkward hand-positioning that occurs during fights.

HOW TO DO IT

- Grasp the bar or handles with one hand facing away from you and one facing behind you.
- Start from a dead hang with your arms fully extended.
- Pull yourself up until your chin is over the bar, then lower yourself back to the start position. Switch your hand positions around with each set.

STRENGTH WORKOUT 6

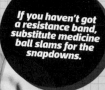

If you haven't got a resistance band, substitute medicine ball slams for the snapdowns.

Your final strength workout is designed to enhance explosive strength using pairs of movements. The first, strength-based move will get your muscles firing, then you'll do an explosive movement following a similar pattern of motion. This will teach you to apply your new-found strength explosively.

EXERCISE	WEEK	REPS	SETS	REST
SUPERSET 1				
1a Bulgarian split squat	1 2 3 4	6 each side 6 each side 6 each side 6 each side	4 4 4 4	
1b Box jump	1 2 3 4	4 4 4 4	4 4 4 4	90sec after 1b 90sec after 1b 60sec after 1b 60sec after 1b
SUPERSET 2				
2a Band press-up	1 2 3 4	10 10 10 10	3 3 4 4	
2b Clap press-up	1 2 3 4	6 6 6 6	3 3 4 4	90sec after 2b 90sec after 2b 60sec after 2b 60sec after 2b
SUPERSET 3				
3a Recline row	1 2 3 4	10 10 10 10	4 4 4 4	
3b Resistance band snapdown	1 2 3 4	6 6 6 6	4 4 4 4	90sec after 3b 90sec after 3b 90sec after 3b 90sec after 3b

1a Bulgarian split squat
Targets Glutes, hamstrings

WHY DO IT

- It's a great move for unilateral leg strength – with the added bonus that doing it with dumbbells will test your grip.

HOW TO DO IT

- Hold a dumbbell in each hand and rest one foot on a bench, instep down.
- Squat down with your leading leg until the knee of your rear leg almost touches the floor, then drive back up. Finish all your reps on one side before switching legs.

1b Box jump
Targets Lower body

WHY DO IT

- It's a classic plyometric move that forces you to be explosive and powerful.

HOW TO DO IT

- Find a stable surface to jump on. A plyometric box is ideal but if you're in a fighting gym, a ring apron works just as well.
- Perform a quarter-squat, then jump up explosively onto the box from both feet at once.
- Step back down rather than jumping to minimise the chance of damaging your achilles tendon.

2a Band press-up
Targets Chest, triceps

WHY DO IT

- It's a great way of adding resistance to a press-up, because it gets tougher at the top of the move, where you should be stronger.

HOW TO DO IT

- Hold a resistance band in your hands and stretch it across your back, then get into a press-up position.

- Perform a press-up as normal. Control yourself on the way down.

2b Clap press-up
Targets Chest, triceps

WHY DO IT

- Clapping between press-ups means you have to push explosively, turning this into a plyometric move ideal for building punching power.

HOW TO DO IT

- Start in a press-up position and lower your chest to the ground.

- Press back up powerfully so that your hands leave the floor. Quickly clap, then land and descend into the next rep.

3a Inverted row
Targets Upper back, core

WHY DO IT

- It's a full-body pulling move, working your core stability at the same time as testing your grip and back muscles.

HOW TO DO IT

- Hang from a bar with your body in a straight line and your feet on the floor.

- Pull up until your chest touches the bar, then lower yourself under control.

3b Resistance band snapdown
Targets Upper back, core

WHY DO IT

- It's a dynamic move that mimics the motion of pulling an opponent down during a clinch, or yanking on their lapel in judo.

HOW TO DO IT

- Tie a resistance band around a pull-up bar or the top of a power rack.

- Hold the band in both hands, then pull it down dynamically. It's fine to use some leg movement.

CONDITIONING WORKOUT 3

Your conditioning workout is the toughest yet: three rounds of nonstop movement, constantly pushing yourself to complete more reps. How much you get out of this workout is up to you – if you can grit your teeth and get through all three rounds, you'll be in fantastic shape.

HOW TO DO THE WORKOUT

- Do ten reps of exercise 1a, then ten reps of exercise 1b. Without resting, go straight back to 1a. Repeat the pattern for a full five-minute 'round'. Count and record how many sets you manage.
- After each round, rest for 60sec before the next one.

EXERCISE	REPS	SETS	REST
ROUND 1			
1a Squat thrust	10	As many as possible	
1b Press-up	10	As many as possible	60sec after 5min
ROUND 2			
2a Divebomber press-up	10	As many as possible	
2b Squat	20	As many as possible	60sec after 5min
ROUND 3			
3a Battling rope slam	50	As many as possible	
3b Sledgehammer swing	10	As many as possible	60sec after 5min

1a Squat thrust
Targets Total body

WHY DO IT

- It's a classic conditioning move – low-skill, easy to do, and an absolute lung-scorcher.

HOW TO DO IT

- Start in a press-up position. Jump your feet forward until they're as close to your hands as possible, then jump them back out again.

1b Press-up
Targets Chest, triceps

WHY DO IT

- It's the classic chest-builder and demands a fair amount of core strength.

HOW TO DO IT

- Hold your body in a straight line with your hands roughly underneath your shoulders.

- Lower yourself until your chest touches the floor, then push back up until your arms are straight.

2a Divebomber press-up
Targets Chest, shoulders

WHY DO IT

- It's a twist on the traditional press-up that works the muscles from different angles, as well as working the flexibility of your hamstrings and lower back.

HOW TO DO IT

- Start with your hands and feet slightly closer together than in a traditional press-up, so that you're almost in an inverted V.
- Bend your arms and lower your chest almost to the floor, then bring it up at the end of the move.
- Reverse the move to return to the start position.

2b Squat
Targets Glutes, hamstrings

WHY DO IT

- It's one of the most fundamental moves you can do and involves some of the biggest muscles in the body. High reps will give you a great cardio hit.

HOW TO DO IT

- Start with your feet shoulder-width apart and slightly turned out.
- Squat back and down as if you're sitting on a chair. At the bottom of the move, your thighs should be parallel to the floor.
- Drive up through your heels.
- Keep your chest up throughout the move.

3a Battling rope slam
Targets **Total body**

WHY DO IT

○ It's a brutal conditioning move that also tests your grip.

HOW TO DO IT

○ Hold one rope in each hand, whip them up in the air, then slam them back down with as much force as possible, squatting down as you do so.

○ Keep a straight back and tight core throughout the move.

3b Sledgehammer swing
Targets **Total body**

WHY DO IT

○ It's an explosive move in which you keep accelerating until you make contact with your target. It also teaches you to use your legs and hips in a move.

HOW TO DO IT

○ Bring the sledgehammer back with your hands far apart on the handle.

○ As you swing the hammer forward, bring your hands together. If you haven't got a hammer and tyre, a medicine ball slam is a good substitute.

FIGHT TO THE FINISH

How to make your workouts effective

If you're stepping up your training, you also need to pay more attention to how you recover, which will let you push yourself harder in the gym, as well as minimising your chances of overtraining.

1 Stay hydrated

Water is the best supplement you can get – it has a huge impact on your training. Aim to take on at least two litres a day or more if you're doing a tough workout. You'll feel the difference in your energy levels.

2 Eat sensibly

Eating badly can undo all your work in the gym. You need protein to fuel your muscles, as well as veg to keep your system healthy. Avoiding sugar and refined carbs will also help. For more nutrition advice see p170.

3 Stay mobile

If you're sore after a tough workout, it's tempting to rest completely. But evidence suggests active recovery – a brisk walk, a slow run or easy bodyweight moves – can improve blood flow and restore you faster.

4 Sleep

The harder you train, the more you need quality sleep. Eight hours a night should be your minimum. To ensure better sleep, make your room as dark as possible and turn off all electronic devices.

5 Warm down

Warming down means slowing towards the end of a session instead of abruptly stopping. Studies suggest this helps eliminate lactic acid and reduce stiffness. Do some gentle foam-rolling or stretching.

6 Listen to your body

Above all, pay attention to the signs of overtraining. If you're irritable, losing your appetite, losing sleep, feeling fatigued or getting ill, it could mean that you've been pushing things too hard without recovering adequately.

FIGHT STYLES

Every style has different strengths and requirements. Find the one that's right for you

BRAZILIAN JIU JITSU

The art of overpowering an opponent with joint locks and chokeholds, practised by UFC champions

Brazilian jiu jitsu (BJJ) has existed since the early 20th century but exploded in popularity in the early 1990s when Royce Gracie, the son of one of its inventors, used it to win three of the first four Ultimate Fighting Championship tournaments. Fighters and fans alike were impressed by the way Gracie defeated larger opponents in the days when weight categories didn't exist.

As a grappling art, it's similar to judo but with the emphasis shifted from throws to joint locks and chokeholds. It works well for self-defence and is an essential skill for MMA (see p80), but there's also a well-established competition circuit where striking isn't allowed and points are scored for gaining positions that would be advantageous in a 'real' fight. You can win at any time by using a submission hold to make your opponent 'tap'.

ROLLING HARD

Thanks to the lack of striking, sparring in BJJ won't give you a concussion and so most gyms include it in every session. This means you'll get fit just by turning up and training, as well as quickly learning what works and what

doesn't. Flawless technique will always beat superior strength, but at the highest levels – where everyone's equally skilful – flexibility, grip strength and endurance are crucial. Some elite fighters do little strength and conditioning work, while others have gruelling regimes. People with almost any body shape can become masters in BJJ by adapting their fighting style to their strengths.

KEY MOVE TRIANGLE CHOKE

In BJJ, being able to defend yourself while on your back – preferably from the 'guard' position, in which you use your legs to control your opponent's movement – is vital. The triangle choke, which involves cutting off an adversary's blood supply by wrapping your legs around their throat (and one arm) in a roughly triangular shape, is one of the style's signature moves.

KEY EXERCISE HIP BRIDGE

It's essential to be able to escape from bad positions such as being 'mounted' – having an opponent sit on you. A good hip bridge helps develop the strength and coordination to get out, especially once you build up to the weighted version.

JUDO

A technique-heavy style that doesn't require huge strength and involves throwing everything but punches

J udo is a relatively young martial art, founded in 1882 by Japanese educator Jigoro Kano as a means to develop better fighters who would also be better people. Though it literally translates as 'the gentle way', you'd be hard-pressed to see why if it's your first time watching a judo match – they're usually a flurry of action, followed by one person being thrown on the floor with quite astonishing force.

But behind that furious grappling there's an enormous amount of technique, and a smaller person can easily throw a much larger one with the right timing and balance. Add in some armlocks and strangles and you've got a sport with skills that are also very useful in a 'real' fight. It's been an Olympic sport since 1964, with recent rule changes that limit groundwork and leg-grab attacks and are designed to emphasise spectacular, spectator-friendly throws.

GRIP AND RIP

Judo training is typically split into two areas – *nage-waza*, or throwing technique, and *ne-waza*, grappling technique. It puts a high emphasis on sparring – or *randori* – which can be exhausting in its own right. But competitive players – as judoka call themselves – need explosive power, gazelle-like balance and the grip strength of a gorilla to be successful, as well as the endurance to keep fighting if the fight goes to 'golden score', the judo version of extra time. They'll also need to be prepared to fight several times in one day: a typical judo tournament might involve the top competitors facing anywhere up to eight opponents, including fights for bronze and silver.

KEY MOVE *UCHI-MATA*

One of the most fundamental throws taught to every judoka, the *uchi-mata* (it translates as 'inner thigh throw') also works at the highest levels of competition – it was the signature move of 2000 Olympic gold medallist Kosei Inoue.

KEY EXERCISE *GI* PULL-UP

Grip fighting is crucial to success in modern judo, and top-class fighters have vice-like strength. The *gi* pull-up – and its civilian sibling, the towel pull-up – build strong forearms for a monstrously tight grip.

MUAY THAI

It's got fists, feet, elbows and knees flying at speed, but the main thing this sport requires is courage

Known in Thailand as 'the art of eight limbs' because it allows strikes with the hands, feet, knees and elbows, Muay Thai also allows strikes from a clinch position, making it one of the most comprehensive stand-up striking styles. It's also known for its devastating kicks – they're emphasised in the scoring, and unlike many other arts, they're allowed virtually anywhere on the body, including the legs.

There's a worldwide competition scene, with various rule-sets that exclude elbows and knees to the face for amateurs. Fights are made up of five three-minute rounds, and traditionally involve the fighters performing a ritual dance – the Ram Muay – before the bout starts, to convey respect for their teachers, warm up and possibly intimidate their opponent. Different versions are done by different fight camps. A band also plays during the fight, intensifying during the later rounds to spur the fighters on.

PEAK CONDITIONING

Muay Thai training usually includes a great deal of shadow boxing, bag work, pad work and sparring. Conditioning is crucial, and serious fighters will toughen up their shins by doing hundreds of kicks on the heavy bag. It's also important to have the cardio endurance to fight for five three-minute rounds, so running, skipping and bodyweight exercises are all popular among Thai fighters. They also pay a lot of attention to the abdominal region, though many fighters are now moving away from the traditional thousands of crunches to more modern methods of training.

KEY MOVE ROUNDHOUSE KICK

Unlike most martial arts, Muay Thai emphasises swinging your whole leg like a baseball bat, and connecting with the shin. This means that, though they're often telegraphed, kicks are painful even when blocked.

KEY EXERCISE JUMP SQUAT

Lasting for five rounds of continuous kicks demands huge explosive power and leg endurance, and jump squats are the perfect prescription. In Thailand, trainers often demand a 180° spin in the air to make sure fighters are getting enough height.

BOXING

Bare-knuckle brawling and gentlemen's fisticuffs combine in this sport of power, footwork and timing

Boxing has existed in various forms since the ancient Greeks included a bare-knuckle fight in the original Olympic games, but ever since the Marquess of Queensberry introduced gloves and rounds – and banned spiked boots – it's been the most popular fighting sport in the world. The amateur and Olympic versions are scored on solid punches landed and emphasise hand speed, footwork and accuracy, while the professional version dispenses with protective headgear, making punching power and resilience more important.

It's also crucial to be skilled in bobbing, evading punches and controlling the ring. Professional bouts can last anywhere from four to 12 rounds, with victory possible via knockout, decision, the three-knockdown rule or an opponent's corner throwing in the towel.

KNOCKOUT POWER

Boxers traditionally relied on long-distance roadwork and bodyweight exercises to stay in shape – partly from fear of going up a weight class – but today's athletes use everything from medicine balls to Olympic lifting to keep them fast and explosive while giving them the endurance to fight for 12 rounds. Boxers also use sport-specific kit such as the speed bag, slip bag and speed ball to develop their reflexes, timing and head movement.

Every MMA fighter practises boxing to some extent, although even UFC stars can't punch with the devastating power boxers build through years of training. The techniques most useful to MMA fighters are offensive ones, since the smaller gloves used in MMA make traditional defensive postures less effective.

KEY MOVE JAB

The jab is used to gauge distance, unbalance opponents and set up power punches or combinations. Counter-punchers try to evade and counter an opponent's jab, while long-limbed fighters can use it to 'lever' open an opponent's defences.

KEY EXERCISE TRICEPS PRESS-UP

Although most boxing strength comes from the legs, having good triceps strength and muscular endurance is still key. Keeping your hands close to your sides during a press-up fits the bill perfectly.

KARATE

Despite its kids-in-pyjamas reputation, karate is at the heart of many top mixed martial artists' skills

Karate, meaning 'empty hand', can be used to refer to dozens of Japanese fighting styles that differ dramatically in their training techniques, tactics and goals. The most popular among pro fighters are *kyokushin*, which emphasises hard sparring with most strikes permitted, and *shotokan*, one of the oldest styles, which is more associated with point-sparring (minimal-contact contests for points).

Both have been used with great success in MMA, though they lend themselves to very different styles of fighting: Lyoto Machida's counter-heavy style is based on *shotokan*, while Georges St-Pierre's explosive striking has its foundations in his early *kyokushin* training.

ART OF THE *KATA*

Traditionally, karate emphasises hundreds of repetitions of basic movements, often in set patterns or *kata* that make them more efficient. Karateka also need excellent flexibility in their hips and legs to deliver efficient kicks, with point-fighting competitions requiring explosiveness in order to deliver punches and kicks and then retreat quickly.

Karate traditionalists sometimes spend hours conditioning their hands by striking a straw *makiwara* or using weighted jars and sandals to build fight-specific strength – but it's possible to emulate this style of training with modern gym equipment. Depending on the style practised, karate can include a lot of sparring. One hallmark of *kyokushin* is the 100-man *kumite*, in which masters take on dozens of opponents in a matter of hours.

KEY MOVE FRONT KICK

The *mae geri* is one of the most commonly used karate kicks, because it can be performed very fast with little wind-up and is very difficult to block. It can be delivered as a powerful thrusting front kick or incorporate more of an upward 'snap', like the kick that Machida used to knock out Randy Couture at UFC 129.

KEY EXERCISE KNUCKLE PRESS-UP

Because traditional karate was designed for fighting without gloves, the knuckle press-up is a staple of many fighters' regimes, designed to strengthen the bones of the hand. It's also possible to do in single-leg and close-grip variations.

WRESTLING

One of the world's oldest sports – and still one of the toughest, demanding serious strength and endurance

One of the oldest organised sports in existence, wrestling has been a part of the Olympics since 648 BC and different versions of it are practised around the world – in India it's known as *pehlwani,* while in Mongolia it's *bokh.* These days, though, you're most likely to encounter it in its two modern Olympic flavours: freestyle, where the object is to throw and pin your opponent, and Greco-Roman, where the aim is the same but trips and leg-grabs are forbidden. Matches are scored using a best-of-three format, with points awarded for takedowns, reversals and exposing an opponent's back to the mat – though it's also possible to win instantly via pin.

PIN TO WIN

Because it involves near-constant physical contact, wrestling is one of the most physically demanding fighting styles in the world. It involves balance, co-ordination strength, power and endurance – and, because of its demanding weight categories, encourages packing them into the most economically-sized frame possible. Wrestlers hit the weights hard, but also employ a variety of bodyweight moves to get used to shifting their own weight, paying special attention to the legs, core and neck. Because it's so gruelling, wrestling provides a great base of mental toughness for other sports – in the words of US Olympic gold medallist Dan Gable, 'Once you've wrestled, everything else in life is easy'.

KEY MOVE DOUBLE-LEG

You won't often see it in high-level competition because it's difficult to pull off against an experienced opponent, but the double-leg is one of the first moves every wrestler is taught, and probably the most spectacular. It's a bit like a rugby tackle, but with more emphasis on getting right under an opponent and using your whole body to upend them.

KEY EXERCISE SPRAWL

Doubling as a variation on the burpee, the sprawl is both a horrible exercise to do for high reps and an exercise in technique. You drop your hips to the floor while keeping your chest and head up, which counters the above double-leg, making it an essential move for every wrestler to learn.

TAEKWONDO

The national sport of South Korea is based around lightning-fast strikes with both feet and fists

The name taekwondo translates literally as 'the way of hand and foot' but this discipline is generally more associated with the latter, since its most spectacular knockouts come from high or spinning kicks. The World Taekwondo Federation's scoring system used in the Olympics, where taekwondo has been a competitive sport since 2000, places most emphasis on kicking – a kick or punch to the body scores one point, but a kick to the head scores three. Punches in the head aren't allowed under WTF rules, though they are in the International Taekwondo Federation, a competing body with similar influence on the world circuit. Both styles have produced fighters that have done well in kickboxing and MMA, thanks to their emphasis on distance, timing and footwork.

SPLITS THE DIFFERENCE

Flexibility is obviously crucial in taekwondo – if you can't kick to an opponent's head, you might as well not compete. Hamstring durability is a constant concern, so strengthening exercises such as the weighted step-up are crucial, with calf raises, lunges and squats all contributing to a top competitor's fitness regime. Rotational power is also helpful, adding power to the art's already-vicious spinning hook and back kicks.

There's less emphasis on upper-body training, but the endurance to compete in several matches over the course of a day is key to tournament success. The timing employed by top-level fighters can allow them to land devastating strikes that can easily knock out an opponent with a single hit.

KEY MOVE AXE KICK

Although it's not traditionally one of taekwondo's central moves, the axe kick – bringing one leg up in a crescent, then chopping it straight down from head height – has increased in popularity during competitions, where it can easily break an opponent's collarbone. It's a surprise tactic, and can be virtually impossible to dodge if delivered correctly.

KEY EXERCISE SINGLE-LEG SQUAT

Taekwondo's emphasis on kicking demands explosiveness, balance and co-ordination, all of which are targeted by this simple bodyweight move.

MMA

The best mixed martial artists bring together elements of all the fighting arts for a sport of devastating power

Technically, this isn't a single martial art but a set of rules under which almost every type of fighting move – the exceptions being dangerous techniques like eye-gouges, groin shots and hair-pulling – is allowed. That said, more and more gyms are offering 'MMA' classes, which usually means they'll be teaching how to combine the moves from different arts: how to mix strikes and wrestling takedowns, say, or how to use Brazilian jiu jitsu submissions when someone's trying to punch you.

Doing everything at once can be confusing, though, so if you're serious about fighting it's best to start with learning one or two separate styles, then putting things together once you've built a strong awareness of the different techniques involved.

ROUGH AND TUMBLE
Because it's a blend of every other fighting discipline, MMA is one of the most physically demanding sports in the world, and participants have to be ready for anything. MMA coaches often try to mimic the constantly changing demands of a drawn-out fight by prescribing circuits containing everything from rope climbing to sledgehammer swinging, as well as incorporating more sports-specific moves such as practising strikes on the ground. It's also more gruelling than other fighting styles because the rounds are longer. A professional fight typically takes place over three five-minute rounds, while main events and title fights increase this to five.

KEY MOVE GROUND AND POUND
MMA is the only discipline in which fighters specifically prepare to pummel a downed opponent. While this might sound relatively easy, it's a more complicated proposition than you might think. The key is maintaining good posture and avoiding submissions – ideally, fighters try to use BJJ techniques to advance to a 'dominant' position before striking.

KEY EXERCISE TYRE FLIP
Manhandling a gigantic tyre is a favourite move in MMA training montages – partly because it looks impressive, but also because it works the whole body while promoting explosiveness.

KICKBOXING

There are many different forms of this style but they all require a combination of speed, skill and flexibility

Kickboxing is a fairly broad term used to describe a group of martial arts that involve kicking and punching, with a variety of rulesets depending on the country and organisation a bout takes place in. Unlike Muay Thai, it doesn't allow clinching and elbows. K-1, one of the most well-known kickboxing organisations, allows knees to the face, but most other federations don't.

Branches include the French *savate*, which only allows certain styles of punch and kick, and the Chinese *sanshou*, which awards points for throws, trips and knocking opponents off the raised platform where it takes place. Some American styles don't allow strikes below waist level, but these are becoming less common.

Kickboxing's more spectacular moves – such as the superman punch or spinning back kick – are also popular in MMA, since opponents wary of takedowns are potentially more vulnerable to such attacks.

KICKING OFF
Like Muay Thai fighters and boxers, kickboxers need to have speed and power, combined with the endurance to throw power strikes for an entire fight. The core and legs need to be powerful to develop the strength to transfer power from the ground and into strikes.

Kickboxers tend to be slightly larger in the upper body than Muay Thai fighters, because of the increased emphasis on punching in their sport. In some federations, including K-1, one-night tournaments are common, so fighters need to be able to pace themselves over up to three fights in a short space of time.

KEY MOVE SPINNING BACK FIST
A 'surprise' punch that can be set up in a variety of ways, and is devastating when landed correctly. It's often thrown in combination with a jab or low roundhouse, to try and catch out an opponent who rushes in after the first move.

KEY EXERCISE LEG RAISE CIRCLES
Kickboxing's huge emphasis on core strength means that abs isolation exercises are popular, but fighters are moving away from doing hundreds of crunches and toward doing other abs moves using slower, more controlled reps.

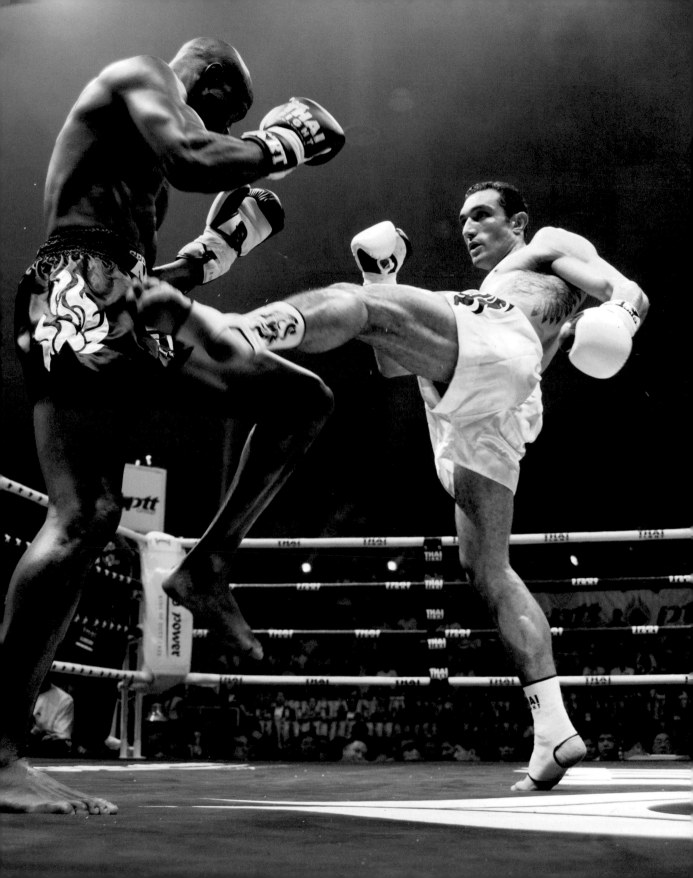

SAMBO

Combining Asian martial arts with boxing techniques adds up to a Russian revolution in fighting

Sambo is a Russian fighting system that's actually a fusion of numerous fighting styles, including jiu jitsu, judo and boxing. It was developed to train the Soviet Red Army for combat – in Russian, the name is an acronym meaning roughly 'self-defence without weapons'– but became recognised as an official sport in 1938 and eventually became the country's national sport.

The two main forms practised today are sport Sambo, which involves throws and submissions, and combat Sambo, which adds standing strikes. Combatants wear a judo-style top, known as a *kurtka*, with shorts and specialised shoes. Chokes aren't allowed, but leg and ankle locks are common, in contrast to most other grappling styles. Sambo isn't as widely practised as BJJ or judo, but has produced some of the world's top fighters, including heavyweight legend Fedor Emelianenko and former UFC champ Andrei Arlovski.

ROLLING HARD

Sambo matches can be gruelling affairs, lasting up to six minutes and shifting from standing to the ground and back again rapidly – if a submission doesn't happen almost immediately on the ground, the combatants are restarted standing. Power, strength and endurance are crucial, and leg strength is especially vital both for throws and defending leg lock attempts. Sambists, as they're known, are often exceptionally flexible and can usually do a full split. Combat Sambo's inclusion of strikes means that fighters need fast reactions and power, as well as the ability to go from striking to clinch-fighting quickly.

KEY MOVE KNEEBAR

A classic submission, in which the Sambist uses the leverage of their entire body to attack an opponent's leg. These aren't legal in Brazilian jiu jitsu until the brown belt level, which means that lower-level grapplers often aren't experienced in defending against them.

KEY EXERCISE KETTLEBELL SWING

Kettlebells have been a mainstay of Russian training for decades, and the traditional swing works all the qualities needed by an elite Sambist – explosiveness, endurance and leg strength.

MMA

Mixed martial arts allows every different fighting style, so its stars are some of the best athletes on the planet. Here are their training secrets

All-round athletes

Mixed martial arts requires incredible fitness. Here's how to get it

E ver since the ancient Olympic sport of *pankration* – a hybrid of boxing and wrestling that allowed trachea-grabbing and groin-kicking – people have been fascinated by the spectacle of mixed fighting styles doing battle. In the late 20th century it was brought to the wider public's attention by the Brazilian Gracie family, who helped to create the Ultimate Fighting Championship, which pitted everyone from sumo wrestlers to ninjas together in a contest to see what worked best.

Now, mixed martial arts is a more civilised affair, with top-flight athletes competing under a recognised set of rules in a series of weight classes. Each fighter is well-versed in every aspect of fighting, from punches and kicks to throws and submissions. That not only means that it's essential to have the strength and speed to pull off all these moves, but also that it's desirable to pack the most power possible into a relatively small frame. In this section, we've consulted some of the world's best mixed martial artists for the secrets of their training.

King Georges

The best fighter on the planet shows off the moves that helped reinvent him

'**T**he key to being good at something and improving at it is to have fun doing it,' says Georges St-Pierre, the current UFC welterweight champion, one of the most dominant UFC fighters of all time and arguably the most well-rounded ever. '**If you're not enjoying it, you won't improve.**' It's good advice that St-Pierre himself had to heed after years of pushing himself physically and mentally, training with some of the best fighters in their respective fields and fighting the cream of the welterweight division.

A knee injury sustained in 2011 gave the man known as GSP the chance to reassess his training and, rather than go back to pushing the biggest weights possible, he took the opportunity to experiment with gymnastics and bodyweight moves. It's made him a more well-balanced fighter – and helped him rediscover the sport he's always loved. 'I'm much faster and more powerful now,' he says, 'and it's not even because I'm trying harder. I'm just having more fun.'

Turn-over for St-Pierre's core workout

GEORGES ST-PIERRE
Age 31
Height 1.78m
Weight 77kg
Achievements
UFC welterweight champion

The key is to have fun. If you're not enjoying it, you won't improve

PART 1
Build a champion's core

Blitz your core with this halo circuit, alternating between dynamic and isometric holds

1 Halo
Time **10 seconds between each other exercise**

WHY DO IT

- It mimics the 'isometric' parts of a fight, like holding an opponent down in side control.

HOW TO DO IT

- Sit in a dish shape, with just your glutes touching the floor, holding the position by contracting your abs.

2 Knee tuck
Reps **10**

WHY DO IT

- It's a classic 'dynamic' abs move.

HOW TO DO IT

- Starting with your back on the floor, crunch up until your knees touch your chest.

3 Spread V-sit
Reps **10**

WHY DO IT

- As well as hitting the core, this move also brings the benefit of some dynamic flexibility.

HOW TO DO IT

- Sit up and raise your legs off the floor, spreading them as far apart as possible.

4 Alternating jackknife
Time **30 seconds**

WHY DO IT

- It's a core move with the added bonus that it challenges your co-ordination.

HOW TO DO IT

- Keeping your arms and legs straight, touch your left arm to your right foot, then repeat on the other side.

5 **V-sit**
Reps **10**

WHY DO IT

- It forces you to keep control in your core, which is useful for grappling.

HOW TO DO IT

- Keeping your legs straight and arms above your head, sit up and raise your legs to form a V.

PART 2
Stay on the ball

'Think of these gym ball moves as a game,' says St-Pierre. 'Once you've learned them, combine them and have fun with them.' However many sets and reps you do, you'll build core strength

1 Compass drive

WHY DO IT

○ It works your core in every different direction.

HOW TO DO IT

○ Holding a ball between your feet, imagine that your head is 'north' on a compass, and touch the ball to north, south, east and west.

2 Oblique twist

WHY DO IT

○ It works your balance from a position you'll often find yourself in if you take part in MMA.

HOW TO DO IT

○ Starting in a press-up position with your shins on the ball, twist to one side and point your top leg towards the floor.

3 V-sit

WHY DO IT

○ It works your core in every different direction.

HOW TO DO IT

○ Holding the ball between your feet, sit up so your body forms a V-shape and pass it to your hands, then lower. Perform another V-sit to pass the ball back to your feet.

4 Body roll

WHY DO IT

○ It forces you to maintain body tension while shifting position, a skill that's vital in grappling.

HOW TO DO IT

○ Holding a ball between your feet and with your arms above your head, roll from your back to your stomach, without letting the ball touch the floor.

POWER CENTRE
Doing these moves gives GSP the core strength required to generate power quickly in the Octagon

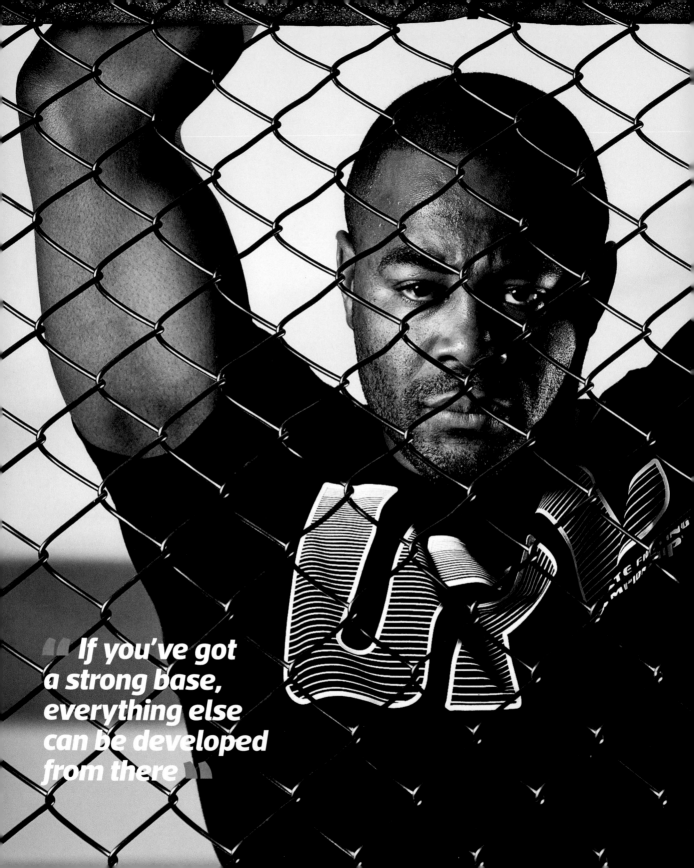

" If you've got a strong base, everything else can be developed from there "

Power shots

Former UFC champion Rashad Evans explains how to train your lower body for one-punch knockout strength

The sport of MMA has evolved considerably since Rashad Evans made his UFC debut in 2005, and Evan's ability to evolve with it has played a huge part in his continued success in the Octagon. With a college wrestling background, Evans spent the early part of this career using his wrestling skills to dominate opponents in the cage, while working diligently to develop his striking outside it.

He announced his arrival as a fully-rounded mixed martial artist in 2008 by knocking out former UFC light heavyweight champion Chuck Liddell with a single punch. He went on to win the title later that year. Although he lost it to Lyoto Machida, he followed that defeat by beating a who's who of the division – including Quinton 'Rampage' Jackson and Tito Ortiz – to earn another shot at the championship.

Asked what the key factor was in his punching power, Evans's answer is instant. 'It's all about your legs. If you've got strong legs and a strong base, everything else can be developed from there.'

RASHAD EVANS
Age 32
Height 1.80m
Weight 93kg
Achievements
Former UFC light heavyweight champion and NCAA Division 1 wrestler

Turn over for Evans's power moves

PART 1
Leg workout

'Do two circuits of these five exercises with no rest between reps or sets,' says Evans's strength and conditioning coach Mike van Arsdale. 'Ride the exercise bike for 3min at 55rpm after the first circuit, then for 10min after the second.'

1 Squat
Reps 16

WHY DO IT
○ The squat is a fundamental strength move that should be part of any legs workout,' says Van Arsdale.

HOW TO DO IT
○ **Stand with your feet shoulder-width apart and your toes pointing out slightly.**

○ **Brace your core and lower yourself by bending at the knees till your thighs are parallel to the floor.**

○ **Maintain natural arch in your back and keep your knees in line with your feet.**

○ **Push back up through your heels to return to the starting position.**

2 Alternating lateral lunge
Reps 8 each side

WHY DO IT
○ 'An MMA fight puts you in some unusual positions. This move builds the ankle stability you need to reduce the risk of injury.'

HOW TO DO IT
○ **Begin with your feet close together and your torso upright.**

○ **Take a big step to your right, keeping your left knee in line with your left foot with both feet pointing forwards.**

○ **As you step out, raise your arms to a horizontal position.**

3 Jumping lunge
Reps 8 each side

WHY DO IT
○ 'Jumping lunges will help to build your cardio, allowing you to fight hard for a full five-minute round.'

HOW TO DO IT
○ **Start in a split stance with your right foot forward.**

○ **Bend both knees, keeping them in line with your feet.**

○ **Jump up and swap leg positions in mid-air, landing in an opposite split stance with your left foot forward.**

○ **Then repeat the lunge.**

4 Jump squat
Reps 16

WHY DO IT
○ 'Jump squats build explosive power, which will help to improve both your punching and your wrestling.'

HOW TO DO IT
○ **Squat down as in exercise 1.**

○ **Push up explosively to jump off the ground, before returning to the starting position.**

COACH'S TIP
'Wear a weighted vest for the first circuit and then take it off for the rest of the workout,' says Van Arsdale

5 Alternating forward lunge
Reps **8 each side**

WHY DO IT

○ 'Alternating forward lunges are great for building unilateral strength, which is useful for MMA because you hardly ever push off from both your feet at the same time.'

HOW TO DO IT

○ Take a big step forward with one foot. Don't allow your front knee to move ahead of your toes.

○ Lunge until your trailing knee brushes the floor. Stand up and repeat on the other leg.

PART 2
Striking technique

Practise these technique moves alongside your leg strength workouts and you'll deliver a knockout blow with your hands or feet

1   Overhand right

'Sit down on your punch and use your hips to generate power,' says Evans. 'You can't bounce around – your legs have to be rooted.'

HOW TO DO IT

○ With your feet planted, spin your right heel and drive your right knee down.

○ Rotate your hips and wind up your right hand.

○ Use the power generated by your hips to swing your right hand over your shoulder and down onto your opponent's chin, while keeping your left hand up to protect your chin from a counter-attack.

2 Right roundhouse kick to the head

'Keep your left hand up as you throw it and bring your back up again straight afterwards in case you miss,' says Evans, who knocked out Sean Salmon with a right roundhouse kick to the head at UFC Fight Night: Evans vs Salmon in 2007.

HOW TO DO IT

- Stand in a fighting stance with your feet shoulder–width apart and your hands up to protect your face.

- Shift your weight on your front leg and kick your right leg in an arched motion from the floor to the target, while whipping your right hand past your hip for momentum.

- Lead with your shin and, when the leg is nearing its target, turn your hip to create more speed and leverage. Make sure you pivot on the ball of your left foot to allow your body to turn with the kick.

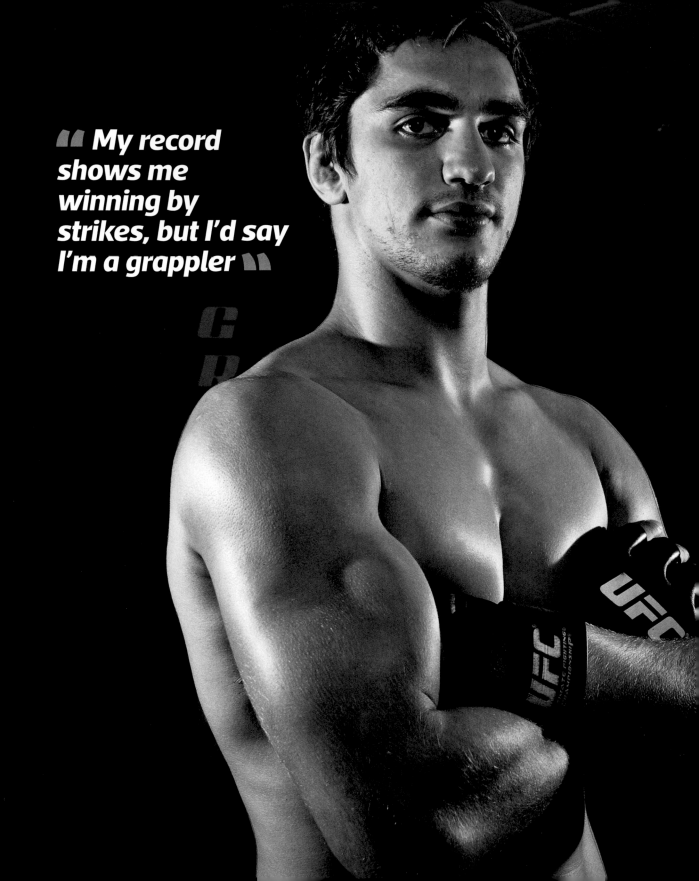

" My record shows me winning by strikes, but I'd say I'm a grappler "

HOOKS

Cardio machine

Develop the conditioning that lets sprawl-and-brawler John Hathaway overwhelm opponents

Few sports demand the same strength, power, conditioning and ability to deal with physical punishment as MMA, but rugby comes close - and welterweight Hathaway credits his experience as a flanker for Hove RFC with preparing him for the UFC. Making his debut at the age of 21, Hathaway put on an impressive performance to stop Irish fighter Thomas Egan in the first round. He's gone on to dominate the likes of *The Ultimate Fighter* season one winner Diego Sanchez, using a mixture of takedowns, solid boxing and vicious ground and pound.

'My record shows me winning by strikes, but a lot of those were from punches on the ground,' says Hathaway. 'I'd say I'm slightly more of a grappler – I come from a rugby background, so I'm using to tackling people.' He's also relentless on the attack, something which comes from the circuits he does at London Shootfighters, a top British MMA gym with a track record of producing above-average takedown artists.

JOHN HATHAWAY
Age 25
Height 1.85m
Weight 77kg
Achievements
Won his first 14 pro MMA fights

> *Turn over for Hathaway's endurance circuits*

PART 1
Barbell workout for grappling strength

Hathaway works on building the endurance to grapple for three rounds if he has to. Do all of these moves without a break to work your grip and cardio

1 Deadlift
Sets 3 Reps 8

WHY DO IT

○ It's the most fundamental full-body strength move, and works your grip and forearms as well as your legs – ideal for grappling.

HOW TO DO IT

○ With your feet shoulder-width apart, grab hold of a bar – use a double-overhand grip, since you aren't lifting heavy. Your shins should be almost touching the bar.

○ Keeping your chest high and driving through your heels, push your hips forward to stand up with the bar. Lower under control.

2 Front squat
Sets 3 Reps 8

WHY DO IT

○ It encourages more quad involvement than the traditional back squat, which is perfect for a powerful wrestling shot.

HOW TO DO IT

○ Power-clean the bar so that it's resting across the front of your shoulders – your fingertips should be supporting it, your elbows pointing forwards.

○ Squat down until your thighs are parallel to the ground, then drive up through your heels.

3 Bent-over row
Sets 3 Reps 8

WHY DO IT

○ It's a compound move that focuses on your all-important back muscles.

HOW TO DO IT

○ Deadlift the bar from the floor, then bend forward at the hips. Pull the bar in towards you until it touches your lower abs.

○ Lower the bar under control.

4 Power snatch
Sets 3 Reps 8

WHY DO IT

○ It's a full-body move that makes you incredibly explosive.

HOW TO DO IT

○ Hold a bar with hands double shoulder-width apart.

○ Drive your hips forward and accelerate the bar upwards until it's above your head and your elbows are locked out.

○ Rest for one minute, then repeat the whole circuit twice.

TURN OVER
for Hathaway's
killer Bulgarian bag
conditioning circuit

PART 2
Bulgarian bag workout for killer conditioning

Do all of these moves without stopping, rest 30 seconds and repeat twice

1 Round the world
Time 30 seconds

WHY DO IT

○ It works the core strength you need for a big double-leg takedown, with the added bonus that it taxes your grip at the same time.

HOW TO DO IT

○ **Hold a Bulgarian bag by the handles and swing it around your head, using your legs and core to power the move.**

○ **Do an equal number of clockwise and anti-clockwise reps.**

2 Pinch grab
Time 30 seconds

WHY DO IT

○ It develops quick reflexes as well as the grip strength to control a moving opponent.

HOW TO DO IT

○ **Using the handle on the top of a Bulgarian bag, yank it up in the air, let go of it and then quickly grab it with the other hand. Try to make the hand-switches as fast as possible.**

PART 3

Barbell moves for rotational strength

Twisting is vital for power-punching. This workout helps

1 Landmine
Sets 3 Reps 10 each side

WHY DO IT

O 'This teaches you to punch with your legs, rather than just arm-punching,' says Hathaway. 'If you focus on the speed of the reps, you'll develop serious punching power.'

HOW TO DO IT

O **Wedge a barbell into either a corner or a weight plate on the ground. Push it forwards as if you're throwing a punch, driving forward with your legs.**

O **Finish all your reps on one side before switching sides.**

2 Wrestler twist
Sets 3 Reps 10 each side

WHY DO IT

O 'This rotational movement, which a bit of a level change, works your whole body and is great for all-round strength,' says Hathaway.

HOW TO DO IT

O **Rotate the bar from side to the side, lowering it to knee height each time.**

O **Most of the force should come from your legs and hips, rather than from your arms.**

3 Jump squat
Time 30 seconds

WHY DO IT

O It's an explosive legs move and the bag mimics the feeling of taking down a real opponent.

HOW TO DO IT

O **With the bag across your shoulders, squat down and then explode up, aiming to get as high as possible.**

O **Land, reset and then repeat.**

Going strong

Build your speed and footwork like UFC star Ross Pearson

The winner of the UK vs USA season of MMA reality TV show *The Ultimate Fighter* knew what he wanted to do at an early age. 'I got my black belt in taekwondo when I was ten,' says Pearson. 'Then I got a brown belt in judo and competed in the nationals, before going into amateur boxing. I always said to my mum and dad I wanted to be a black belt in every martial art.' With such a strong base in a variety of fighting styles, mixed martial arts was the obvious career choice for the young fighter, and his stint on *TUF* secured him a slot in the UFC, where he now fights at featherweight.

Pearson's known for his nonstop fighting style, aided by pushing himself to the limit in the gym. 'It's horrible,' he admits. 'Sometimes it feels like you're going to puke up a lung. It's just constant go, go, go. But as painful as it is, I like training and I'm mad for the sport. Even if I was only fighting on the little shows, I'd still do it. I just love the test and knowing that I'm the best I can be.'

> *Turn over for Pearson's strength and conditioning circuits*

ROSS PEARSON
27
1.73m
66kg

The Ultimate Fighter
season 9 winner

" *As painful as it is, I like training and I'm mad for the sport* **"**

PART 1
Pulling and pushing

Pearson builds strength by lifting heavy and doing tough variations of bodyweight moves. Do these moves with plenty of rest between sets

1 Weighted dip
Sets 3 Reps 5

WHY DO IT

○ The classic triceps strength builder. 'Bodyweight dips are good, but you can make them harder by adding weight,' says Pearson. 'If you haven't got a belt, hold a dumb-bell between crossed ankles.'

HOW TO DO IT

○ Start with arms straight, then lower yourself until your upper arms are parallel to the floor.

○ Push back up until your elbows are locked out. Leaning forward will work your chest harder, while staying upright will work your triceps.

2 Clinch-grip pull-ups
Sets 3 Reps 8

WHY DO IT

○ As well as all-over strength, this improves your grip. 'I train my grip strength by doing pull-ups with a set of thick handles, suspended for extra instability,' says Pearson. 'You can make your own by wrapping towels around a pull-up bar. By strengthening your grip you'll be able to lift heavier weights.'

HOW TO DO IT

○ Start from a dead hang position with your arms straight.

○ Pull up until your chin is above the bar or handles.

3 Rack pull
Sets 3 Reps 5

WHY DO IT

○ 'You should be able to get more weight on the bar in this than you would in a deadlift. It lets you work on similar muscles without risking your lower back as much.'

HOW TO DO IT

○ Start with a bar loaded on the pins in a power cage. You should be aiming for similar weight to your max deadlift.

○ Drive your hips forward as you lift the weight.

4 Bulgarian split squat
Sets 3 Reps 5 each leg

WHY DO IT

○ 'Unilateral moves are important. In fighting or any sport, you're unlikely to be pushing off both legs at the same time, so training to push off one leg explosively is vital.'

HOW TO DO IT

○ Start with your instep on a bench behind you, holding a pair of weight plates or dumbbells in your hands or a bar across your back.

○ Bend your lead knee until your back knee brushes the ground, then straighten up. Finish your reps on one side before you do the other side.

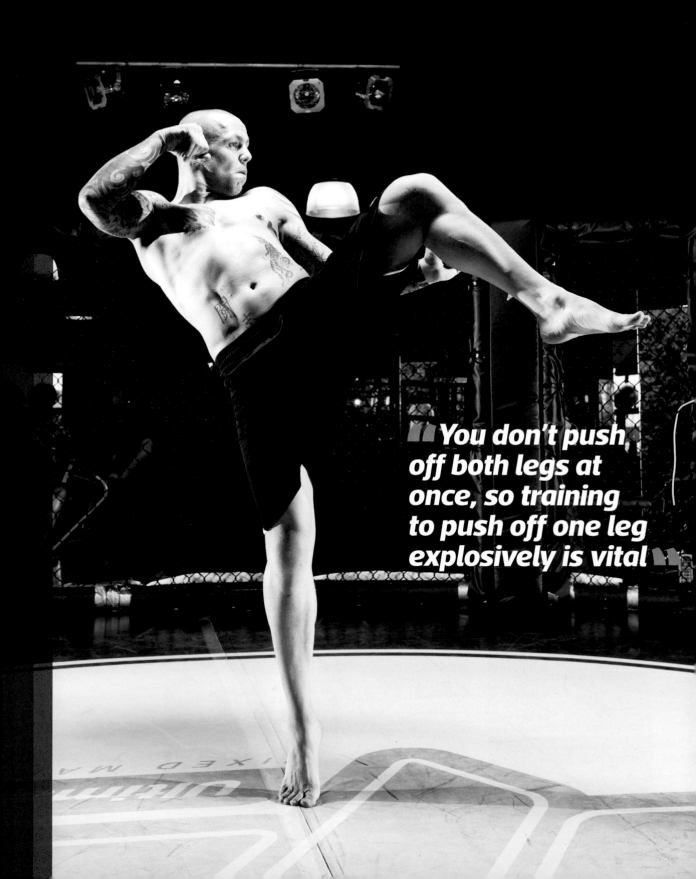

You don't push off both legs at once, so training to push off one leg explosively is vital

PART 2
Fight conditioning

Pearson never stops moving – in the gym or in a fight. Perform the following moves with 20 seconds' rest between sets for a lung-scorching cardio workout

1 Fast feet and sprawl
Sets 5 Time 30 seconds

WHY DO IT

- These skills are key to MMA. 'I do this on a mat because it makes it tougher,' says Pearson. 'If you haven't got one, just do it on the floor.'

HOW TO DO IT

- Run on the spot, focusing on moving your feet as fast as possible.
- Every few seconds, 'sprawl' by throwing your feet back and dropping your hips to the mat, keeping your chest up.
- Pop back up to your feet and carry on running.

2 Ground and pound
Sets 5 Time 30 seconds

WHY DO IT

- 'This really gets you used to the feeling of fighting a tough opponent.'

HOW TO DO IT

- Straddle a grappling dummy or punch bag with a resistance band secured above you.
- Throw straight punches, elbows and hammerfists – known as 'ground and pound' – working against the resistance of the bands.

3 Punch and sprawl
Sets 5 Time 30 seconds

WHY DO IT

- 'You've got to learn to sprawl quickly after a combination if you're going to fight in MMA, and even if you aren't this is great for cardio.'

HOW TO DO IT

- Throw a combination – a quick jab, cross, hook is ideal.
- Immediately after the last punch, sprawl (see exercise 1).
- As you get more comfortable with the move, turn as you sprawl – this makes it more difficult for you to be taken down.

4 Super burpee
Sets 5 Reps 10

WHY DO IT

- 'This gets you used to the level changes you need in a fight, and it's really tough.'

HOW TO DO IT

- Drop into a press-up position, do a press-up and then jump back to your feet.
- As soon as you're on your feet, explode into a tuck jump, bringing your knees to your chest. Focus on height rather than just getting easy reps – it'll pay off in the ring.

PART 3
Sudden impact

Pearson explains how to perfect your striking techniques with moves they'll never see coming

1 Superman punch

WHY DO IT

○ 'It's a great surprise technique,' says Pearson. 'I threw this when I beat Dennis Siver in 2010 and followed it up with a headkick.'

HOW TO DO IT

○ **Throw out a jab to confuse your opponent and block their view.**

○ **Pick your rear leg up off the ground as if you're about to throw a roundhouse, but instead drive off your front leg to spring forward.**

○ **Throw a punch with your rear hand as you jump forward.**

2 Cross, hook, headkick

WHY DO IT

○ 'Throwing a headkick in MMA can finish a fight with one strike.'

HOW TO DO IT

○ **With your left foot forward, throw a right cross by twisting at your hips and pivoting on the ball of your right foot.**

○ **Throw a hook by twisting your hips the other way and bringing your elbow level with your shoulder.**

○ **Twist your hips to fire a full-power kick at your opponent.**

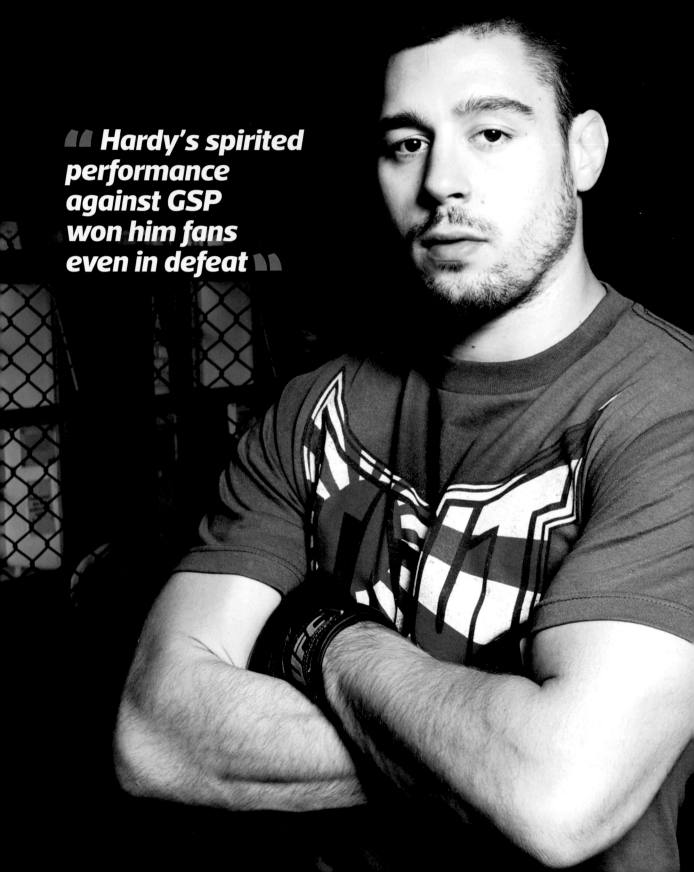

" Hardy's spirited performance against GSP won him fans even in defeat "

Hard to hit

Get knockout power like welterweight contender Dan 'The Outlaw' Hardy

One of the most impressive entries on Dan Hardy's fight CV is 'first ever British UFC title challenger'. After going on a four-fight win streak as soon as he entered the promotion, he put on a spirited performance at UFC 111 against dominant champ Georges St-Pierre that won him fans even in defeat. Now Hardy's making his way back up the ladder, becoming a more well-rounded fighter as he goes.

Hardy has one of the more varied martial arts backgrounds in the UFC, with everything from a youthful interest in taekwondo to a training visit to China's famous Shaolin temple in his experience. He's combined it all into an unpredictable striking game that's dangerous even against elite-level kickboxers, as seen in his left-hook knockout of Duane 'Bang' Ludwig in May 2012. But he's not just a one-trick pony: he's worked with coaches as different as rubber-guard innovator Eddie Bravo and NFL conditioning specialist Joe DeFranco in an effort to round out his game, and continues to improve.

DAN HARDY
Age 30
Height 1.83m
Weight 77kg
Achievements
Former UFC welterweight title challenger

Turn over for the secrets of Hardy's knockout power

Do moves based on putting force production into motion as fast as possible

PART 1
Core strength

A strong midsection lets you transfer power through the ground and into your fists and feet. Here's how Hardy builds his

1 Core twist
Sets 3 Reps 8 each side

WHY DO IT

- 'I get abdominal endurance from sparring and drilling,' says Hardy. 'To get high force, I do strength training moves like this one.'

HOW TO DO IT

- Wedge an Olympic barbell into a corner or into a heavy plate on the floor.
- Holding the barbell with both hands, rotate your trunk. The movement should feel similar to throwing a punch.

2 Dragon flag
Sets 3 Reps 5

WHY DO IT

- 'The important thing with this is to stick to a slow tempo – but be warned, like most eccentric movements it can make you a bit sore.'

HOW TO DO IT

- Holding on to a solid object such as a bench or squat rack, bring your legs up as you would in a leg raise.
- Lower your legs as slowly as possible. You should aim to spend four or five seconds on the eccentric (downward) part of the move.

3 Medicine ball slam combo
Sets 3 Reps 5

WHY DO IT

- 'This works your posterior chain like a deadlift, but it's based around speed and putting that force production into motion as fast as possible.'

HOW TO DO IT

- Jump up and slam the ball to the ground as hard as possible, as if you're doing an aggressive slam dunk.
- Pick it up or catch it on the bounce, then throw it backwards over your head at a wall or partner.

4 Medicine ball throw
Sets 3 Reps 5

WHY DO IT

- 'This move will improve your ability to produce force through a specific range of motion, and help you to develop knockout power.'

HOW TO DO IT

- From a fighting stance, throw the ball at a wall by pivoting on the ball of your back foot, twisting your rear hip forward and firing your arm forward as if throwing a punch. Repeat on the other side.

PART 2
Fight conditioning

Hardy trains his whole body with big, compound moves. Here's how you can do the same

1 Farmer's walk
Sets 4 Distance 40m

WHY DO IT

○ 'This is the only real bit of strength endurance that I do,' says Hardy. 'It trains my grip and upper body, which are key in jiu jitsu.'

HOW TO DO IT

○ Grip a weight in each hand and walk as fast as you can. If you haven't got room to walk in a straight line for 40m, do laps.

○ If you don't have the kit, wrap towels around the handles of dumb-bells. To start, try 25kg in each hand.

2 Rope climb
Sets 3 Reps 3 (5m rope)

WHY DO IT

○ 'This is a great way to increase your pulling strength as well as grip. You can always do it wearing a weighted jacket to make it more difficult too.'

HOW TO DO IT

○ Try to climb the rope without using your legs, and do three or four big pulls rather than lots of little ones.

○ If you haven't got a rope, throw a towel over a pull-up bar and grip the ends. Aim for eight to ten pull-ups per set.

3 Smith machine jump squat
Sets 5 Reps 3

WHY DO IT

○ 'Moving the bar as fast as possible will activate your high threshold motor unit. The right load will be 20-30 per cent of your one-rep max back squat.'

HOW TO DO IT

○ On a Smith machine, sink into a quarter-squat before exploding upwards into a jump as fast as possible.

○ The load on the bar should be just heavy enough to let you get through your reps without slowing down.

4 Sled drag
Sets 3 Distance 20m

WHY DO IT

○ 'To work my posterior chain, I use a variation of the sled drag that eliminates the eccentric phase which can lead to muscle soreness.'

HOW TO DO IT

○ Back away from the sled holding the strap until you're bending over, in a similar position to the deadlift.

○ In one explosive move, straighten up and pull the sled towards you.

PART 3
Finish strong

Hardy explains how to perfect your striking techniques

1 Spinning back kick

WHY DO IT

- 'I used to use this a lot in my taekwondo days. David Loiseau finished his fight against Charles McCarthy with one at UFC 53'.

HOW TO DO IT

- Start in a fighting stance – left or right foot forward – then turn and look over your opposite shoulder.
- Your feet pivot with you, and you fire your right leg back behind you. As you strike, look over your shoulder to see where it lands.

2 High-low combination

WHY DO IT

- 'When you move forward your opponent will be expecting you to come with a jab, so the unexpected angle can catch him out.'

HOW TO DO IT

- Put your left foot forward and throw a long-range uppercut.
- Twist your hips and throw a right hand.
- As you bring your right hand back, move your right leg forward and kick the inside of your opponent's front leg with your left foot.

Striking distance

Train like UFC middleweight Michael Bisping, who combines endurance with fast-twitch knockout power

Leading the British charge into the UFC, Michael 'The Count' Bisping first made his mark by tearing through the competition en route to winning season three of *The Ultimate Fighter.* He made his debut at light heavyweight, putting together a string of 14 wins before losing on a split decision to Rashad Evans and dropping to middleweight. He's known for overwhelming opponents with relentless volume-punching and cardio, but he himself almost seems surprised that his opponents aren't in the same shape as him.

'You can never guarantee you're going to win a fight,' says Bisping. 'That's out of your control. But you can make sure you turn up in condition to go the full distance. When I'm training I might feel like I'm dying, but you've got to push yourself through that barrier – that's what takes you to the next level. A lot of people quit when it gets too hard, and that's what makes a difference. They'll take a breather and slow down - that's fine in the gym, but not when someone's trying to beat you up.'

> *Turn over for Bisping's cardio workout*

MICHAEL BISPING
Age **33**
Height **1.88m**
Weight **84kg**
Achievements
The Ultimate Fighter
season three light heavyweight winner

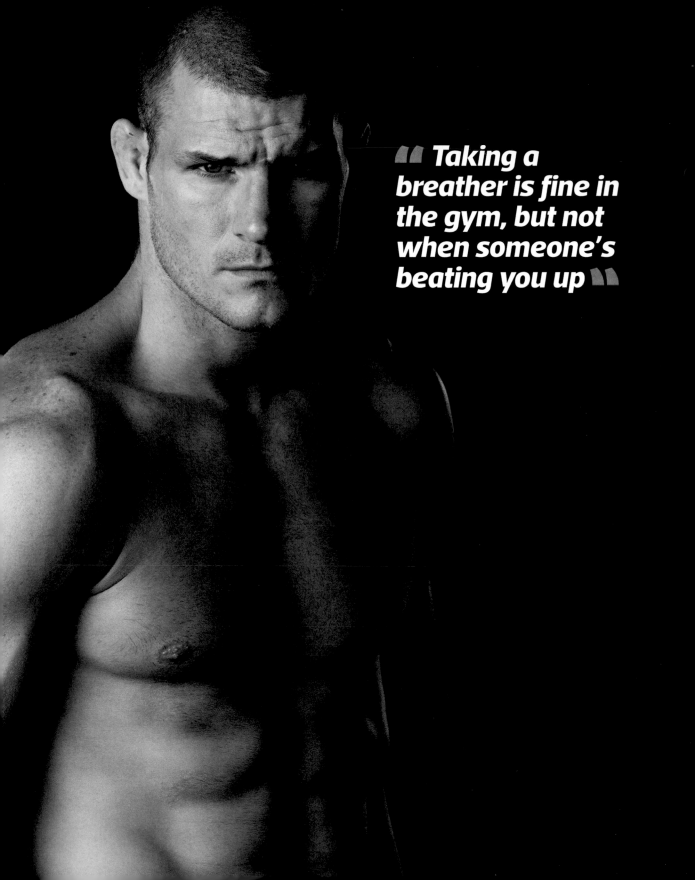

"Taking a breather is fine in the gym, but not when someone's beating you up"

PART 1
Full-body explosiveness

Whether you're striking or grappling, the ability to explode at an instant's notice is critical. Ensure you're ready with this circuit

1 Clap press-up
Sets 3 Reps 10

WHY DO IT

- 'These give you the explosive strength you need to fire off a big punch,' says Bisping.

HOW TO DO IT

- Start at the top of the press-up, then descend quickly until your chest is just above the floor and explode upwards.
- Clap at the top, and aim for as much height as possible.

2 Bag spin
Sets 3 Reps 8

WHY DO IT

- 'This simulates the movement of picking up an opponent for a big takedown. Use a bag well below your own bodyweight to start with.'

HOW TO DO IT

- Pick a punchbag up off the floor, lifting with your knees and keeping your back straight.
- Spin the bag in front of you like a propeller, first one way then the other. Start with 180° spins. Move up to 360° if it's too easy.
- Put the bag down between repetitions.

3 Bunny hop
Sets 3 Reps 10

WHY DO IT

- 'We do these as part of our warm-up. They'll get you ready to start kicking things.'

HOW TO DO IT

- Start on the balls of your feet.
- Bend your knees until your thighs are at least parallel to the floor.
- Jump as far forward as you can without losing your balance. Land on the balls of your feet again.

4 Knee bound
Sets 3 Reps 10

WHY DO IT

- 'This is a slightly more advanced move that really gets your hips working. Make sure you do it on a soft floor.'

HOW TO DO IT

- Start in the same position as the bunny hop.
- Drop forwards onto your knees, then drive forwards with your hips and jump forward.
- Land on the balls of your feet and repeat.

"Spinning the bag simulates picking up an opponent for a big takedown"

PART 2
Fight conditioning workout

Do these moves back to back to get in shape for a nonstop brawl

1 Sprawl
Sets 3 Reps 10

WHY DO IT

- 'This is the most basic way to defend against a man who's trying to tackle you to the floor,' says Bisping. 'It looks simple, but it takes years to perfect.'

HOW TO DO IT

- **Starting from a boxing stance, kick your legs backwards, drop your hips and catch yourself on your hands.**

- **Get your hips close to the floor, but keep your chest up and keep looking straight forwards.**

- **Jump back up to your feet.**

2 Shuttle run
Sets 5 Reps 10

WHY DO IT

- 'We use these to finish off a training session – intense sprinting is better than distance running for the sort of cardio you need in the Octagon.'

HOW TO DO IT

- **Pick a distance so you'll be able to do the full set at a fast pace. Between 10m and 20m should work.**

- **Sprint to one end of the course, touch the ground and sprint back. That's one rep.**

3 Bounce knee
Sets 3 Reps 25 each side

WHY DO IT

- 'Throwing Muay Thai knees is harder than you think. Using weights means it's an arm workout too.'

HOW TO DO IT

- **Raise two 5kg dumbbells above your head, then bring them down to your hips as you throw a knee by pushing your hips forwards and up.**

- **Try to find a rhythm, bouncing as you throw alternate knees and resting as little as possible.**

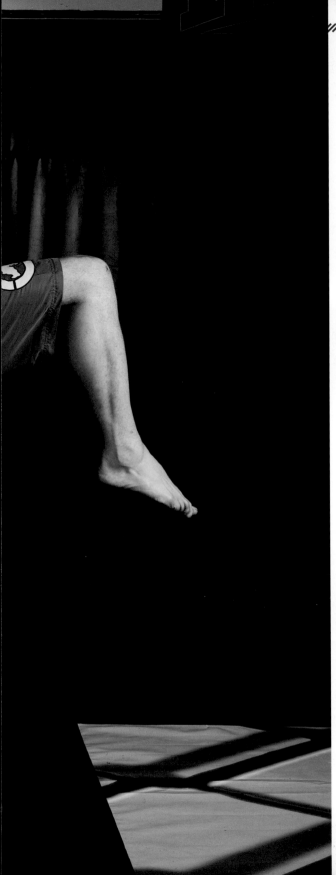

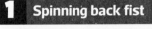

PART 3
Knockout blows

Bisping explains how to perform his signature striking techniques

1 Spinning back fist

WHY DO IT

○ 'This takes people by surprise. I throw it if my opponent is dropping his hands or getting sloppy.

HOW TO DO IT

○ **Throw a right cross to distract your opponent and get your hips ready.**

○ **Step forward and rotate quickly, aiming to strike with your knuckles or forearm.**

2 Flying knee

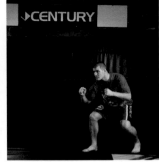 

WHY DO IT

○ 'This is the move I used to knock out Ross Pointon in the semi-finals of *The Ultimate Fighter*. The idea is to take your opponent by surprise.'

HOW TO DO IT

○ **Bring your non-kneeing leg up as you jump, then drive it back as you strike. Keep your toes pointed at the ground and your legs bent.**

○ **If you're in a real fight, aim for your opponent's chest or chin.**

Knockout artist

Discover how power puncher Paul Daley stays in shape to deliver vicious KOs

Plenty of fighters can deliver a knockout with a flurry of punches or a single well-timed shot, but no-one in MMA has made a career out of the one-punch KO like British super-striker Paul Daley. After starting karate at the age of eight, he diversified into kickboxing during his teens. A string of knockout wins brought him to the UFC in 2009, where he blasted submission specialist Dustin Hazelett and fellow striker Martin Kampmann into unconsciousness en route to a title eliminator bout with wrestler Josh Koscheck. Unfortunately, Daley's desire for a knockout got the better of him and he threw a punch after the bell, resulting in an unceremonious discharge from the UFC.

Since then, the Nottingham-based fighter has been collecting scalps wherever he can. 'I'm always improving,' says Daley. 'I've got good movement, I've got power, I can kick, knee, elbow, punch and I can throw crazy moves. Basically I can do it all and I'm going to continue to develop into one of the best there ever was in the sport.'

Turn over *for Daley's knockout routine*

PAUL DALEY
Age **29**
Height **1.75m**
Weight **78kg**
Achievements
14 kickboxing wins, Cage Rage welterweight champion,

"I can kick, knee, elbow, punch and throw crazy moves. I can do it all"

PART 1
Endurance circuit

Having the confidence that he can fight out of bad positions lets Daley be extra aggressive. Do each of these moves without rest, take one minute's break and then repeat for two more 'rounds'

1 Divebomber press-up
Time 30 seconds

WHY DO IT

- It's a more taxing version of the standard press-up, and brings your shoulders into play more.

HOW TO DO IT

- Get in a press-up position with your hands and feet slightly closer together than normal, so your back is arched in the air.
- Perform a press-up, 'diving' through so that your face almost touches the ground. Return to the start position.

2 Sprawl
Time 30 seconds

WHY DO IT

- This mimics the movement you'd use to stop a wrestler from tackling you – getting your legs away from them while using your bodyweight to stop them from driving forwards.

HOW TO DO IT

- Starting from a normal fighting stance, drop your hips towards the floor. Keep your chest and head up.
- Pop back to your feet explosively.

3 Bridge
Time 30 seconds

WHY DO IT

- This is one of the most fundamental ways of escaping from underneath an opponent who's on top of you in 'mount' or 'side control' position.

HOW TO DO IT

- Lie on your back, with your feet close to your glutes.
- Push up explosively to form your boy into a bridge shape, bringing your hips off the floor. You can either bridge straight up, or alternate sides, looking over each shoulder.

4 Alligator press-up
Time 30 seconds

WHY DO IT

- This taxing version of the press-up teaches you to keep your weight low – perfect for controlling a grounded opponent.

HOW TO DO IT

- Starting in the top of a press-up position, bring one knee up as you move the opposite hand forwards. Keep your hips as close to the ground as possible.
- Keep walking forward, performing a press-up with each step.

PRO ECBO IN

5 Wrestler get-up
Time 30 seconds

WHY DO IT
○ Wrestlers know you shouldn't fight from your knees, so the endurance to keep getting up is essential. This builds it.

HOW TO DO IT
○ **Start kneeling on the floor. Stand up with one leg, then the other, briefly moving into a squat position.**

○ **Kneel down again, one leg at a time.**

6 Sit-out
Time 30 seconds

WHY DO IT
○ This is a move that wrestlers typically use when an opponent sprawls on top of them – it lets them escape and, potentially, reverse the position.

HOW TO DO IT
○ **Start on all fours, facing downwards. Take one hand off the floor, and kick the opposite foot underneath your body.**

○ **Return to the start position and repeat on the other side.**

PART 2
Close at hand

Unlike boxing, MMA doesn't get broken up when you enter the clinch. Because of that, it's important to be comfortable fighting from close range so you don't burn your arms out. Use this mini-circuit to practice the transition between the two – repeating each move five times for one 'round'

1 Pummelling
Time **30 seconds**

WHY DO IT

○ Getting an 'underhook' on your opponent allows you to control them. This helps.

HOW TO DO IT

○ **Starting with one arm under your opponent's armpit and the other on their biceps, try to work your free arm under their opposite arm.**

○ **Aim to clasp your hands behind your opponent's back and stop him from doing the same to you, since it's a position that leaves you vulnerable to a takedown.**

2 Padwork
Time 30 seconds

WHY DO IT

○ Precision striking is hard enough when you're fresh, but it's much harder when you're tired. Switching between the two helps you keep your guard up.

WHY DO IT

○ Go straight from pummelling to striking, getting a partner wearing focus mitts to call out combinations. He should push the pace and make you work.

○ Depending on how comfortable you are with striking, ask him to throw half-speed strikes back. This should encourage you to keep your hands up when you're tired.

Legend of the Octagon

Two-division champ and Hall Of Famer Randy Couture talks about training, fighting and just who hit him the hardest

Any discussion about the greatest MMA fighters of all time has to include Randy Couture, but the man known to fans as Captain America came into the sport at an age most fighters are thinking about hanging up the gloves. After a lengthy wrestling career, he made his MMA debut at 33, winning two matches in a one-night UFC tournament. He went on to become heavyweight champ on two separate occasions before dropping to light heavyweight, defeating Chuck Liddell to take that title as well. After a memorable trilogy of bouts with Liddell and a flirtation with retirement, he reclaimed the heavyweight belt again before finally closing out his career at light heavyweight. He retired at 47 to focus on an acting career and coaching younger fighters.

Q *In today's environment, would you have taken up MMA earlier or still pursued the dream of being an Olympic wrestler?*
I chased the Olympic dream for so long and it was such a big part of my life that I think I'll always be a wrestler at heart. But I've had so much fun with MMA. The end of my wrestling career was quite frustrating – I was still physically able to compete, but the changes I was making in my style were very minute and incremental, whereas MMA was this new sport and every time I worked out I learned something new.

Q *The sport has changed hugely since the early days of your career. What's your craziest memory?*
The first UFC I fought in was UFC 13 in Augusta, Georgia. Nobody in the crowd knew anybody on the card, they were just there to see some scraps. My wife at the time, Trish, was sitting up in the stands, and there was a whole row of guys in front of her with probably six teeth between them, and they were all fired up. Their banter made her so nervous she had to run outside and throw up. There were more fights in the stands that night than there were in the cage!

Q *What was the toughest fight of your career and who hit you the hardest?*
The toughest fight for sure was my first fight with Pedro Rizzo. He kicked me 14 times in my left thigh and when I got to the locker room it was swollen and black and I couldn't walk properly for about six weeks. He broke my nose too. It was a rough-and-tumble, back-and-forth battle and a really tough fight. In terms of who hit the hardest, it had to be Chuck Liddell. I've been knocked on my can a few times, but there's a difference between that and getting properly knocked out, where you're there one second then the next you're going, 'Who the fuck are you guys?' Chuck had that rare quality.

Q *How did you adapt your training as you got older?*
As you get older you refine your tactics and your training and stick to the things that are getting results. There's a fine line to walk, because if you've gone too hard doing weights, sprinting or doing plyometrics in the morning that you can't perform in the sparring sessions in the evening you're going to have problems.

Q *Do you still train much?*
I do more strength and conditioning, maintenance-style training now. I still get on the mats, but I do less sparring and more grappling. When I was in Sofia for the *Expendables 2* shoot I had a friend there who I was able to grapple with once or twice a week. It's a lifestyle and it doesn't feel right unless you get your time in the gym.

Q *What do you miss most about competing?*
The training, especially training camps. I've got a great staff who take up all the slack and allow me to train twice a day, eat, sleep – life becomes very simple. You establish a strong bond with the team when you're punching each other in the face and beating each other up. They're unique guys.

Q *Would you swap one of your UFC titles for an Olympic wrestling gold... or an Oscar?*
I think things work out the way they're supposed to. If I'd won an Olympic medal I'd never have had the opportunities I got down the road.

BOXING

The art of pugilism demands power, speed, accuracy and co-ordination. Here's how its stars put them all together

Heavy hitters

Boxers pack awesome punching power into agile frames. Here's how it's done

From Jack Johnson and John L Sullivan to Muhammad Ali and Mike Tyson, boxers have always been some of the toughest and most respected athletes on the planet. Not only do they need strength, speed, power and endurance, but they need to combine the aforementioned traits with abs of steel and an iron jaw. And more importantly than any of that, they also need a mind that can interpret an opponent's patterns and adapt on the fly.

Boxers have traditionally relied on a huge amount of long, slow distance running and bodyweight moves, but in the modern era many pugilists have moved beyond that to take advantage of the latest advances in training theory. Today's champions doing plyometrics as well as press-ups, sprint as well as jog, and squat as well as hitting the speed bag. And even if you don't want to get into the ring, you can take advantage of their training secrets to build your own knockout physique.

King cobra

Strike like a snake with help from IBF super middleweight champion Carl Froch

In a sport where nobody wants a loss on their record, Nottingham super middleweight Carl Froch is something of an oddity: he guns for the toughest, most skilled pugilists in his class and studiously avoids the easy fights, and is just as happy putting on a tactical masterclass as digging in for an all-out war.

As you'd expect from a man who regularly takes on – and beats – the world's best fighters, Froch works as hard in the gym as he does in the ring. 'To win a fight, you need to be strong and explosive with good stamina so you can throw hard punches in every round,' Froch says. 'Because boxing is weight-governed, it's important to do strengthening exercises that don't add bulk, so I don't use fancy equipment or weights.'

Froch does classic bodyweight moves such as press-ups, crunches and dips - 'as many as 300 of each in a session,' he says, 'because volume equals strength. I include variations so my body never gets used to my workouts because shocking your muscles keeps forcing them to get stronger.' He also does skipping, hill climbs and sprints to improve his leg strength and cardio endurance.

Turn over for Froch's endurance circuit

CARL FROCH
35
1.85m
76.2kg

IBF super middleweight champion
Former WBC super middleweight champion

"You need to be strong with good stamina so you can throw hard punches in every round"

PART 1
Press-ups

Strengthen your hands, arms and chest with this tough circuit.
Do each move in turn, rest a minute and repeat twice

1 **Wide press-up**
Reps 30

WHY DO IT

- This press-up variation puts more emphasis on your chest, challenging your muscles from a fresh angle.

HOW TO DO IT

- Your hands should be wider than shoulder-width apart.
- Keep your body straight from head to toe, and look forward as you perform the move.

2 **Fist press-up**
Reps 20

WHY DO IT

- It'll strengthen your fists for hitting the bag, as well as keeping your wrists ready for powerful punching.

HOW TO DO IT

- Keep the same wide grip as before.
- Brace your core as you perform the move and stay on your toes.

3 **Finger press-up**
Reps 10

WHY DO IT

- It's a challenge for your balance and control – and your fingers.

HOW TO DO IT

- Do the move on a gym mat to reduce the load on the ligaments in your hands.
- If you're struggling, do half the reps with your knees touching the floor.

4 **Clap press-up**
Reps 5

WHY DO IT

- In this explosive move, aim to get as much height as you can to develop knockout power.

HOW TO DO IT

- Push up explosively to give yourself enough air time to perform the clap.
- Sink down as you hit the ground to avoid jarring injuries.

❝ I include variations to shock my muscles and force them to get stronger ❞

PART 2
Sit-ups

Build a boxer's abs with this comprehensive core circuit. Do each move, rest a minute and repeat twice

1 Sit-up
Reps **40**

WHY DO IT

O It's the classic boxer's move. Focus on doing quality reps with your abs, rather than wrenching yourself up and straining.

HOW TO DO IT

O **Keep your hands touching your head throughout the move.**

O **Keep your head off the floor throughout the move.**

2 Cross-arm crunch
Reps **30**

WHY DO IT

O Keeping your hands folded across your chest ensure you use your abs to power the move, and work harder.

HOW TO DO IT

O **Keep your head off the floor and cross your arms in front of your chest with your fists above your pecs.**

O **Only come up half as far as you do for the sit-up.**

3 Bicycle crunch
Reps **15 each side**

WHY DO IT

O It'll give balance to your abs, working your obliques alongside your rectus abdominis.

HOW TO DO IT

O **Turn your entire upper body as you twist to either side.**

O **Bend your knee on the side you're twisting towards and try to keep the other one straight.**

4 Half sit-up
Reps **10**

WHY DO IT

O It keeps your abs under tension because you're forced to use them to keep your back from touching the floor.

HOW TO DO IT

O **You need to start this as if you're halfway through the rising part of the move.**

O **Keep your upper back off the floor throughout the move.**

PART 3
Pull-ups

Pull-ups build endurance and balance out the pushing you're doing. Rest a minute between sets

PART 4
Dips

Finish strong, with a dip circuit that'll help you keep your hands up in the final round

---

1 Wide-grip pull-up
Sets 4 Reps 10

WHY DO IT

O Pull-ups give you powerful back muscles, allowing you to retract punches just as quickly as you throw them.

HOW TO DO IT

O Start each pull-up with your arms fully extended.

O Raise your chin above the bar and keep your legs crossed to avoid swinging.

---

1 Dip
Sets 2 Reps 15

WHY DO IT

O Dips are a classic triceps builder, and have the bonus of forcing you to tense your abs to get the most possible reps out.

HOW TO DO IT

O **Drop down until the bar is parallel to your lower ribs.**

O **Keep your legs straight for balance.**

---

2 Leaning dip
Sets 2 Reps 15

WHY DO IT

O Leaning forward doing a dip increases chest involvement, giving you powerful pecs.

HOW TO DO IT

O **Lean forward so your upper body is at roughly 40° to the vertical.**

O **Cross your legs and raise them behind you (knees bent at 90°) to ensure your upper body keeps working hard.**

I don't need fancy equipment to build the power, speed and agility I need

DeGale Force

Unleash the storm like Olympic gold medallist James DeGale

Not too many people thought James DeGale would become middleweight champion at the 2008 Beijing Olympics. Bookies were offering odds of 80-1 on the southpaw from northwest London, who as a chubby ten-year-old earned the unflattering nickname 'Chunky'. But thanks to his natural speed, power and burgeoning tactical skills, DeGale was able to see off all his opponents, including tough Cuban Emilio Correa in the final.

DeGale went pro in December 2008, starting in the six-round bouts that are traditional for new professionals – but he's soon moved up to 12-rounders, including a victory over Piotr Wilczewski to take the European super middleweight title. He's something of a training traditionalist, doing long runs to build a base of stamina and using of bodyweight moves for endurance. In the gym his training is all about short, sharp movements that develop his co-ordination, reaction speeds and explosive strength. 'We don't need fancy equipment or heavy weights,' says DeGale. 'We use low-weight strength-building moves, old-school gym kit and lots of partner-based exercise to help me build the power, speed and agility I need to smash my opponents.'

JAMES DEGALE
Age **26**
Height **1.85m**
Weight **76.2kg**
Achievements
Olympic gold medallist 2008
European super middleweight champion

Turn over **to go the distance like DeGale**

PART 1
Speed drills

Think fast so you can move fast, with these lightning-quick drills. Do them before any kind of strength or endurance work so you're fresh

1 **Blind clap punch**
Sets **5** Reps **6**

2 **Obstacle drills**
Sets **3** Time **90sec**

WHY DO IT

○ 'By thinking about speed you're priming your body to go super-fast, and you can use this visualisation technique in the ring,' says DeGale. 'The randomness keeps your reactions sharp.'

HOW TO DO IT

○ Get into a boxing stance in front of a heavy bag, with your eyes closed and a training partner standing close by.

○ Visualise throwing a burst of six jabs at superhuman speed. Whenever your partner claps, open your eyes and try to do exactly that. For each rep, your partner should change the time he leaves before clapping.

WHY DO IT

○ 'Moving around the obstacles as fast as you can without touching them forces you to develop quick, controlled footwork, which is vital when you're trying get away from or close down an opponent.'

HOW TO DO IT

○ Scatter six pieces of kit on the floor over a 2x2m area. Get into a boxing stance, then start moving around the obstacles, bouncing on your toes all the time, changing the direction you face every few bounces.

○ Stay light on your feet and keep changing the route you take around the pieces of kit.

3 Skipping intervals
Sets 6 Time 30sec

WHY DO IT

○ 'Skipping improves co-ordination, timing and foot speed, and intervals prepare me for the periods of lower and higher aerobic intensity in every round. The double- and triple-unders train me to be more explosive.'

HOW TO DO IT

○ Skip gently for 30 seconds to warm up. Go hard for 20 seconds, swapping between crossovers, side swings and speed steps, then skip gently for ten seconds before taking a 30-second break.

○ Once you're more confident, add double- and triple-unders.

PART 2
Power moves

Get power without bulking up with these core-intensive moves.
Do all your sets of each one before moving on to the next.

1 Bar rotation
Sets 3 Reps 20

WHY DO IT

○ 'Bracing your core forces your abs to transfer power between your upper and lower body. That's vital for punch strength,' says DeGale.

HOW TO DO IT

○ In a boxing stance, hold a bar across the back of your shoulders.

○ Brace your core, then, leading with your left hand, twist your body as far as you can to the left, pivoting on your feet. Repeat to the right. Each twist should be fast but controlled.

2 Fist-less shadow boxing
Sets 3 Time 1min

WHY DO IT

○ 'By limiting the power you can generate from your arms, this exercise forces you to use your hips and legs to drive your punches which makes them harder.'

HOW TO DO IT

○ Get into a boxing stance with your fists held up to either side of your chin.

○ Keeping your hands by your head, throw jabs, uppercuts and hooks.

3 Medicine ball single-arm press
Sets 2 Reps 10 each side

WHY DO IT

○ 'The extra resistance will help you make big strength gains in pectorals, biceps and triceps. The result is powerful shots.'

HOW TO DO IT

○ Lie on the floor with your legs bent and your right hand on your right knee. Hold a small medicine ball in your left hand with your arm bent at 90° and your palm facing up.

○ Have a partner stand above you and push down on the ball as you try to press it up.

PART 3
Agility and endurance

Boxers need to be able to change direction quickly and have the ability to throw hard shots on a split second's notice. Develop both skills with these moves and drills.

1 Sweeping lunge
Sets 3 Reps 10 each side

WHY DO IT

- 'This strengthens the hams and glutes so you can keep bobbing and weaving throughout a fight,' says DeGale. 'The sweeping adds instability, which helps improve your balance.'

HOW TO DO IT

- From a boxing stance, bring your leg forward and sink into a deep lunge, sweeping your back hand forward at the same time so it almost touches the floor.
- Push off your front foot. Repeat on the other side.

2 Bench jump combo
Sets 2 Time 1min

WHY DO IT

- 'Doing this as fast as you can boosts strength endurance, your aerobic fitness and your muscle reaction speed.'

HOW TO DO IT

- Straddle a bench, then jump up, landing with both feet on to the bench.
- Drop your left foot back to the floor.
- Hop over so your left foot is on the bench and your right on the floor, then jump up so both feet are on the bench.'

3 Medicine ball abs slam
Sets 3 Reps 15

WHY DO IT

- 'Body blows are often more damaging than head shots. This will condition your abs to cope with them.'

HOW TO DO IT

- Lie in a half-crunch with your fingers locked behind your head and legs bent. Your partner should stand above you holding a medicine ball.
- Get him to throw the ball at your stomach with moderate force, catch it on the bounce and then throw again. Keep your abs braced throughout the move.

You think your talent will take you through, but you need to work on everything

Feel the wrath

Amir Khan, 2004 Olympic hero and two-time world champion, shares the secrets of his reinvention

It was Amir Khan's defeat to Breidis Prescott in September 2008 that turned his career around. After being sent to the canvas in less than a minute by the Colombian bruiser, putting an end to an 18-fight win streak, he decided to reassess his training, work on his weaknesses and reinvent himself. The result? He won his next eight fights, taking the WBA light welterweight world title along the way.

'After that defeat, I changed the way I box, the way I eat, the way I act,' explains Khan. 'I was overconfident and didn't push myself in training. You think your talent will take you through, but you need to work on everything as you improve.'

Working with trainer Freddie Roach and conditioning expert Alex Ariza, Khan rebuilt his body. Instead of a bulky, top-heavy physique, he developed his legs for stability, explosiveness and power. 'I used to work on strength,' says Khan. 'But I got too big, and the big chest and arms were slowing me down. It uses so much oxygen to keep the muscles going.'

To construct his new 'pyramid' physique, he ditched heavy deadlifts and bench presses in favour of intensive circuits that build fast, functional, fluid movements with a mixture of ballistic moves, plyometrics and static holds. 'It's lots of short, sharp movements to work my fast-twitch fibres,' he says. 'It's bang-bang-bang, really intensive stuff. I'm more powerful and quicker now. I can hit and move. I box the way I'm meant to box.'

AMIR KHAN
Age 25
Height 1.78m
Weight 64kg
Achievements
Olympic silver medallist
Former WBA light welterweight champion

Turn over for Khan's fight circuits

Khan's circuit for boxing power

Khan uses intensive circuits to strip fat, sculpt lean muscle and build explosive speed and power. 'Aim for completeness,' says Khan's coach Alex Ariza. 'It's no good having speed and no power, or strength and no balance.' Do each of these exercises for 30 seconds, then moving straight to the next move. After finishing the circuit, rest for one minute and repeat three times.

1 Barbell punch–out

Taking an upright barbell, punch the bar out in rapid bursts, switching arms after five punches. Recruit power from your legs and core as well as your arms.

2 Explosive press–up

With one hand on a Bosu ball and the other on the floor, lower yourself, then explode upwards and to the side so that your opposite hand is now on the Bosu. Repeat.

3 Wall ball

Holding a medicine ball, squat down then explosively jump up and throw the ball up against a wall. Lower into a squat as you catch the ball and repeat.

4 Static hold

With your feet on a gym ball and your hands holding a wobble board or Bosu on the floor, hold the position with your back straight.

5 Medicine ball slam

Lift a medicine ball high above your head, then slam it down onto a mat. Repeat.

6 Farmer's walk

With the heaviest dumbbells you can manage in each hand, walk along a 10m line and back to build shoulder strength and core stability.

Illustrations Sudden Impact

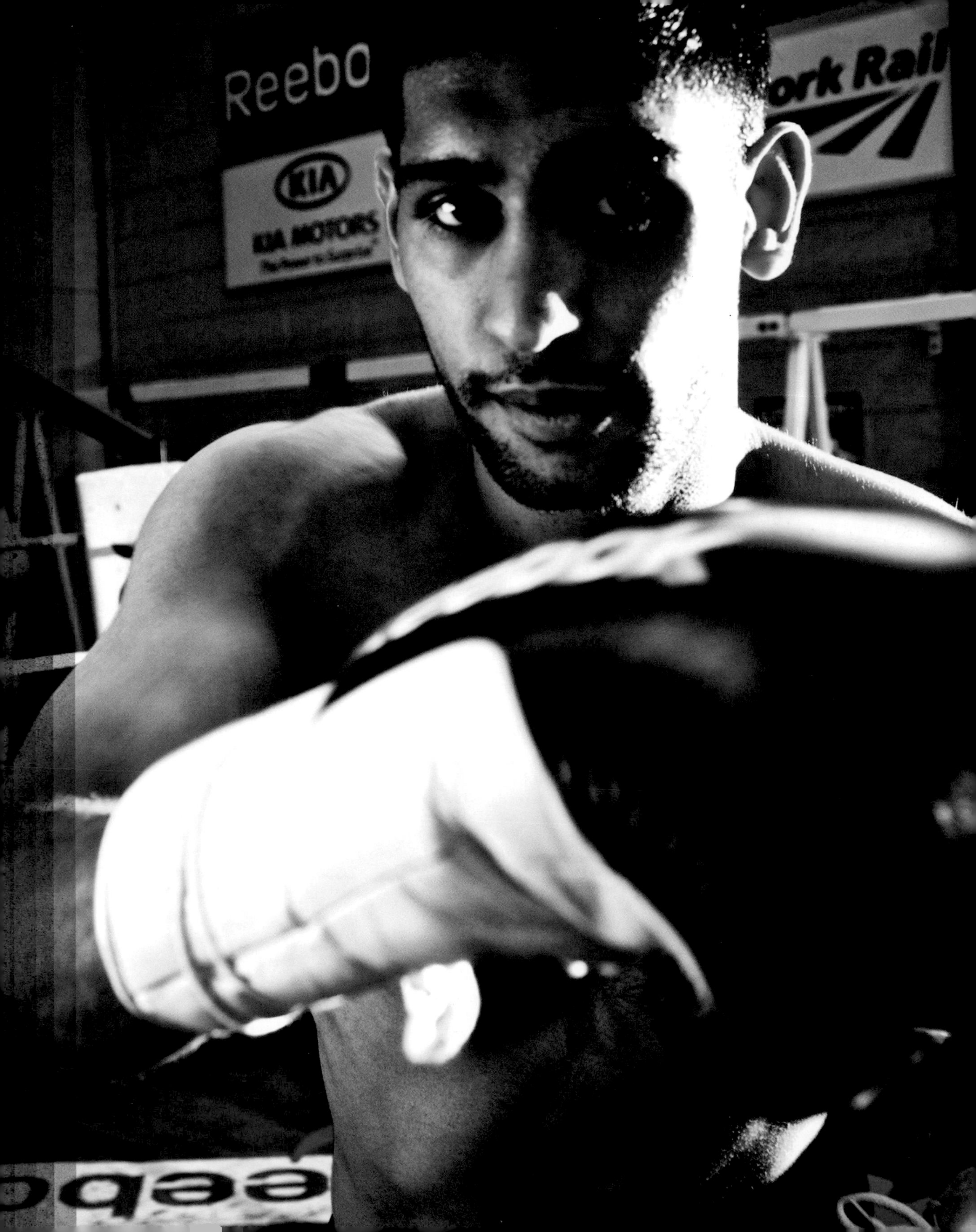
Reebo
KIA
KIA MOTORS
ork Rail

Ring master

Five-weight world champion Sugar Ray Leonard on the real Rocky, his admiration for Amir Khan and why life is like one big boxing match

When it comes to all-time boxing greats, Sugar Ray Leonard's credentials are second to none. Following a stellar amateur career that saw him capture Olympic gold at the 1976 games, Leonard won world titles in five different weight categories as a professional – from welterweight all the way up to light heavyweight. During this run, he achieved notable wins over fellow International Boxing Hall of Fame inductees Tommy Hearns, Marvin Hagler and Roberto Duran, making the stone-fisted fighter quit between rounds. Leonard established himself as the most dominant middleweight fighter of the 1980s, a period widely regarded as the greatest of all time for the division.

Q How fit are you these days?
I still work out pretty much every day. I love running. I love doing cardio. I hate lifting weights but I do light weights just to keep toned. I also play tennis and golf.

Q You were coached by the great Angelo Dundee, who also trained Muhammad Ali. What did you learn from him?
He said the right things at the right time. When I fought Tommy Hearns back in 1981, after the 12th round, Angelo saw the scorecards and said, 'You're blowing it'. He wasn't panicking but there was a sense of urgency because there were just a few more rounds left. I always valued the way we communicated.

Q You came out of retirement in 1987 to beat the formidable Marvin Hagler. What was most satisfying about the win?
It was overcoming the odds. The odds were totally against me. I had been away from the ring for three years and I was a smaller man [than Hagler], but that fight symbolises the power of the mind – that's what it took to beat someone like Hagler, to not give up and to stay focused.

Q You appeared on boxing TV show The Contender with Sylvester Stallone. He's known for the iconic role of Rocky, but is he a genuine fight fan?
Sly is a major boxing fan. I've been to his home and we've watched fights. He's quite knowledgeable and I think the *Rocky* movies showed that – [Stallone knows] what it takes for a guy to be a champion even though he doesn't have all the talent. He has heart and drive and intense fortitude, and that's why *Rocky* was a great inspirational film.

Q Have you seen British light welterweight Amir Khan fight?
I've seen Amir fight a couple of times. I was impressed with the way he came back from his loss against Breidis Prescott with a vengeance and became more confident. He's got great hand speed. He just has to continue to put his punches together and make them shorter to be more successful and more effective. I've always been impressed by what he brings to the table.

Q When you were young, did you have any heroes outside boxing?
Bruce Lee was an idol of mine. Bruce was a small man, powerful, compact and you saw the intensity, concentration and conviction of conquering. I wanted to emulate that because he was so smooth, scientific and fast. He had so many wonderful attributes that I wanted to gain.

Q Is it true you're a fan of MMA and a friend of the Gracie family who pioneered the sport?
Rickson Gracie's a friend. He and I went to Japan for personal appearances together many years ago. And I've talked with Royce about his plans and his vision. Those guys are special – their family changed martial arts. The impact of their style and methods was amazing. Royce, you know, his presence is so unassuming, he's so approachable and he doesn't look ferocious. That's what I like about him because he could take a head off if he wanted to.

Q What else do you do now?
I do a lot of motivational speaking and in my speeches I stress the power of winning. I call it POWER, which means Prepare, Overcome, Win Every Round. I use boxing as a metaphor, because I think we're all fighters in some sense. You get knocked down in the ring and you get knocked down in life. You have to be focused inside and outside the ring.

SUGAR RAY LEONARD
Age 56
Height 1.78m
Achievements
Olympic gold medallist
Former WBC and WBA
welterweight champion,
WBC middleweight
champion, WBC super
middleweight
champion, WBC light
heavyweight
champion, WBA light
middleweight champion

COACHES

Behind every great fighter there's a great coach.
We've got workouts from two of
the best in the business

Storm force

Martin Rooney is a renowned MMA coach who's trained in numerous fighting styles. Build cardio fitness and torch fat with his Hurricane Training method

'There's a horrible trend in training right now that you always go for circuits to the death,' says coach Martin Rooney. 'You get guys who measure the effectiveness of a workout by whether it leaves them lying on the floor feeling crushed. I'm measuring heart rate, weight, body fat – I'm looking for improvement.'

Instead of smashing his athletes into the ground with endless circuits, MMA strength and conditioning expert Rooney has developed his own training system that emphasises rest as much as hard work. 'If you wear a heart rate monitor during a fight, you see it's not max heart rate for 15 minutes – there are periods of recovery,' he explains. 'So I created a system that mimics that exactly.'

He calls it Hurricane Training – for good reason. 'What is a hurricane?' asks Rooney. 'It's a powerful storm that's very brief but leaves destruction in its path. People come back stronger from it and rebuild. And that's what these workouts are designed to do.'

Turn over **for Rooney's destructive workouts**

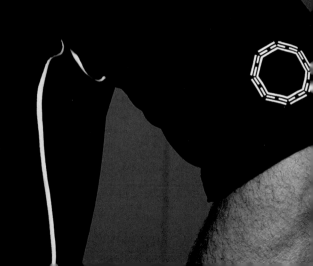

A fight is not max heart rate for 15 minutes – there are periods of rest

Category 1

In the first training stage, Rooney makes sure his athletes have a solid base of fitness before the real storm hits. 'I don't care if you're seasoned, you have to have a baseline,' he says. Set a treadmill at 16km/h and a 10% incline, jump on and sprint for 25 seconds, then get off. Wait until your heart rate returns to 120bpm before getting back on the treadmill. Perform nine sets. After a couple of weeks – longer if your heart rate takes minutes to recover – move up to Category 2.

Category 2

'Once you're conditioned and I know you're not going have a nervous system meltdown and throw up, we can move up to the next stage,' says Rooney. 'From now on there are two exercises performed between each sprint, and you rest as needed.' At this stage, stick to bodyweight exercises. 'Nothing too stressful – you're getting used to using your body and mind in a fatigued state.'

INTERVALS 1–3
Medicine ball press–up, V–sit
INTERVALS 4–6
Lunge, mountain climber
INTERVALS 7–9
Press–up, squat

Category 3

After the first two stages is when you do the bulk of your training, using a weighted barbell alongside sprints to build strength and cardio. Follow the workout over the next three pages to experience a typical Category 3 Hurricane.

HOW TO DO THIS WORKOUT

- *Each Category of Hurricane routine contains nine intervals in total, with three in each round. Each of the rounds should take around five minutes to finish, so the workout lasts 15 minutes – the length of an MMA fight.*

- *Choose a cardio activity – Rooney recommends the treadmill, but sprints and skipping work too. The workout consists of nine 25-second intervals of this activity with a superset of two exercises between each interval.*

- *After three cardio intervals, change the exercises you're doing to make sure you tax your entire body. Do the same after another three intervals. The moves get less demanding with each round so that you can keep pushing yourself without risking injury.*

CATEGORY 3 WORKOUT

Intervals	Exercises
1–3	Close-grip snatch, overhead jerk
4–6	High pull, bent-over row
7–9	Standing triceps extension, standing barbell curl

1a Close-grip snatch
Sets 3 Reps 10

WHY DO IT

- It's a simplified cousin of the classic Olympic snatch – you won't be able to use as much weight as you normally would, but it's easier to do.

HOW TO DO IT

- Hold the bar in front of your thighs with your hands roughly shoulder-width apart.

- Lift the bar powerfully, ducking under the bar to 'catch' it with straight arms at the top of the move.

- Stand up straight.

1b Overhead split jerk
Sets 3 Reps 10

WHY DO IT

- It lets you shift more weight than an overhead press, while also testing your legs.

HOW TO DO IT

- Hold the bar at the top of your chest, in the position you would use for an overhead press.

- Drop into a lunge at the same time as you push the bar upwards, and 'catch' it with straight arms.

- Stand up straight, and lower the bar to begin the next rep.

Category 3

The second and third supersets of your Category 3 Hurricane workout. The moves get less complex and involve fewer muscle groups so you can keep up the intensity without risking injury from your form breaking down as you fatigue. You can substitute in your own moves while following Rooney's principles.

2a High pull
Sets 3 Reps 10

2b Bent-over row
Sets 3 Reps 10

WHY DO IT

O It works your upper back muscles, while also forcing you to stabilise yourself, giving you a core workout.

HOW TO DO IT

O With your hands shoulder-width apart, explosively pull the bar up to your collarbone, allowing your elbows to come out to the sides.

O Lower the bar under control.

WHY DO IT

O It balances out all the pushing you do in your boxing workouts and give you a strong, stable back that'll help you with pressing moves.

HOW TO DO IT

O Lean forward at the hips, keeping your back straight. Tense your core muscles to stabilise your body, and grip the bar with your hands shoulder-width apart.

O Squeeze your shoulder blades together and pull the bar in to your sternum. Lower slowly to the start position.

3a Standing triceps extension
Sets 3 Reps 10

WHY DO IT

○ It's a classic triceps move, and the added benefit of doing it overhead is that you're forced to work your core.

HOW TO DO IT

○ Hold the bar overhead, keeping your body upright.

○ Bring the bar behind your head without leaning forwards, then 'pull' it back to the top of the move.

○ If this hurts your wrists with a barbell, use an E-Z bar or substitute in a different move.

3b Standing barbell curl
Sets 3 Reps 10

WHY DO IT

○ It's a textbook biceps builder and will finish off your workout without overtaxing your nervous system.

HOW TO DO IT

○ Stand tall with your shoulders back and core braced, holding the bar with your hands just outside your hips.

○ Curl the bar upwards without rocking back to gain momentum. Lower slowly to the start.

Category 4

Now things are getting tough. 'This is where you'll start to use heavy resistance exercises,' says Rooney. 'The weight should be relatively light because you'll be tired.'

1–3
Bench press, pull-up
4–6
Weighted dip, barbell curl
7–9
Weighted lunge, dumb-bell pullover

Category 5

'There have been very few documented Category 5 hurricanes,' says Rooney. 'Likewise, I use this sparingly, for our guys to test themselves – we won't do it in the run-up to a fight.'

INTERVALS 1–3
Tyre flip, sandbag lift
INTERVALS 4–6
Rope pull, towel chin-up
INTERVALS 7–9
Farmer's walk, sled push

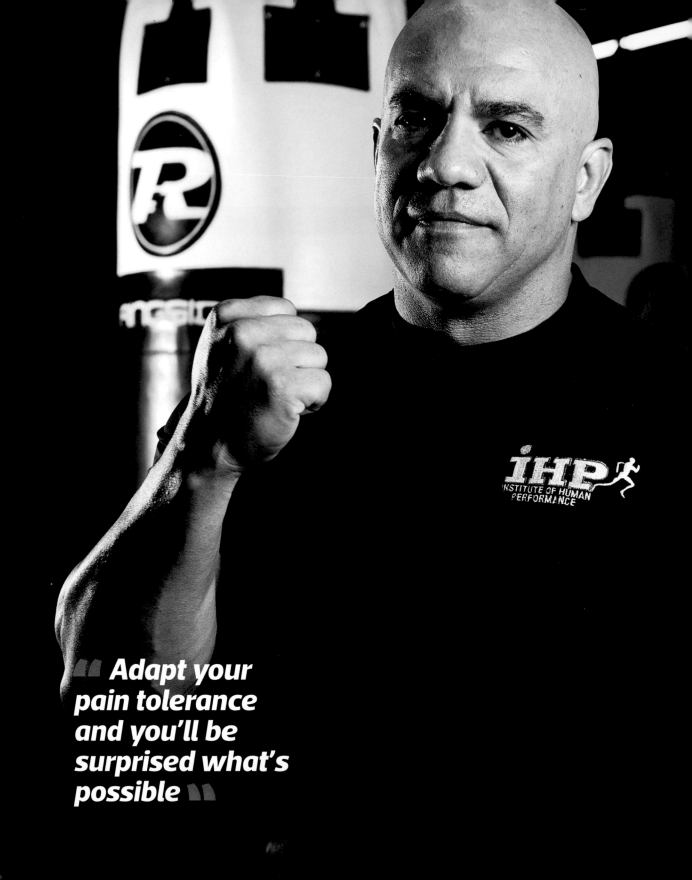

Adapt your pain tolerance and you'll be surprised what's possible

High intensity

JC Santana is one of the world's leading strength and conditioning coaches. Use his MMA circuits to torch fat and get in shape fast

'My job,' says JC Santana, 'is to allow you to hurt a lot without freaking out.' This might seem like a strange statement coming from a man who's spent a decade working with Olympians, soldiers and fighters – from four-weight boxing world champion Robert Duran to leading UFC welterweight Thiago Alves – in his Florida facility, the Institute of Human Performance. These guys are used to pushing themselves without complaining, but Santana takes them to the limit.

It's not that he believes in brutal training for the sake of it – in fact he professes to hate coaching that assumes more is always better. He limits his most punishing sessions to once a week. 'I call it "touching the curtain",' he says. 'I'll tell my athletes that their limits aren't a wall, they're a curtain. I don't want them to go through the curtain – I just need them to touch it. The fastest adaptation you can make is to your pain tolerance. Get through that and you'll be surprised what's possible.' The workout on the following pages will help.

Turn over for Santana's cardio-building circuit

Fight circuit

'I don't want you losing a decision and going 'Man, I could have fought two more rounds,' says Santana. 'I want you winning and then collapsing.' Prepare yourself with this killer circuit

1 Gym ball hyper
Time 30 seconds

WHY DO IT

○ It's a great lower back move with an element of instability.

HOW TO DO IT

○ Lie with your stomach on a gym ball and your feet on the floor.

○ Raise and lower your upper body under control, keeping your core braced.

2 Gym ball reverse hyper
Time 30 seconds

WHY DO IT

○ It's another lower back move that also works your glutes.

HOW TO DO IT

○ Lie with your stomach on a gym ball and your forearms on the floor, taking most of your weight.

○ Raise your legs until they're in line with your upper body, then lower them to the floor.

3 Band chest press
Time 30 seconds

WHY DO IT

○ It's a chest move that works through the same range of motion as a punch.

HOW TO DO IT

○ Stand with one foot ahead of the other as if you're about to throw a punch.

○ Hold a band secured to something in your rear hand and 'punch' forwards. Switch hands with each set.

4 Alternating band pull
Time 30 seconds

WHY DO IT

○ For vital pulling and grip strength, and to retract punches faster.

HOW TO DO IT

○ Stand bent at the hips, holding a resistance band or cable attachment in each hand.

○ Pull the band with one hand and then the other, trying to bring the band to your chest.

HOW TO DO THIS WORKOUT

- Pick ten out of the 15 moves. Try to aim for a balance between pulling, pushing and hip-hingeing moves.
- Do each move for 30 seconds, at the highest intensity you can manage. Allow 15 seconds to switch between moves.
- Do all ten moves back to back, then rest for a minute, the length of time between rounds in an MMA fight. Repeat for two more rounds.

5 Recline pull
Time 30 seconds

WHY DO IT
- It works your grip, core and back muscles.

HOW TO DO IT
- Hang from a bar or a pair of thick handles with your heels on the floor and your body in a straight line.
- Pull yourself up until your chest is in line with the handles, then lower yourself again. Depending on the size of the handle, you may need to use a thumbless grip.

6 Hanging knee raise
Time 30 seconds

WHY DO IT
- It's a killer abs move and using slings means you won't have to drop off the bar when your grip gives out, shifting the focus to your abs.

HOW TO DO IT
- Hang from a pair of slings or a pull-up bar and raise your knees to your chest. Try not to swing.

7 Reaching lunge
Time 30 seconds

WHY DO IT
- It's a classic leg move, tweaked to emulate a wrestling-style pick-up.

HOW TO DO IT
- Holding a medicine ball, step forward into a lunge, and reach forward until you touch the ground with the ball.
- Don't let your front knee move ahead of your toes.
- Step back and repeat on the other leg.

8 One-arm plank
Time 30 seconds

WHY DO IT
- It's a much tougher version of the classic plank, and also works your shoulder stability.

HOW TO DO IT
- Get into the top position of a press-up and lift one hand, keeping both hips an equal distance from the floor. Hold for 30 seconds.
- Either switch hands halfway through or change which hand you're using between sets.

9 Band rotation
Time 30 seconds

WHY DO IT

- It works your abs muscles in a standing position.

HOW TO DO IT

- Standing with a resistance band or cable held in both hands – the resistance should be pulling you to one side – perform rotations.

- Don't try to turn more than about 45° and keep your hips still if possible to work your core.

10 Medicine ball press–up
Time 30 seconds

WHY DO IT

- It adds instability to the classic press-up, making the move tougher and requiring more explosiveness.

HOW TO DO IT

- With one hand on the medicine ball and the other on the ground, do a press-up.

- Pass the ball to the other hand and repeat.

11 Lateral reaching lunge
Time 30 seconds

WHY DO IT

- It's another lunge variation that builds strength for wrestling.

HOW TO DO IT

- Holding a medicine ball in both hands, lunge to the side and touch the ball to the floor.

- Repeat to the other side.

12 Sprawl
Time 30 seconds

WHY DO IT

- It's a crucial wrestling move that's also a tough test of cardio.

HOW TO DO IT

- From a fighting stance, kick your feet backwards and drop your hips as low as possible towards the ground, catching yourself on your hands.

- Jump back up to your fighting stance, then repeat.

13 Cable woodchop
Time **30 seconds**

WHY DO IT
- It works the twisting strength you need to throw a punch or pull off an explosive takedown.

HOW TO DO IT
- Stand with your feet slightly wider than shoulder-width apart, holding a cable attachment.
- Chop across your body from high to low. For an extra challenge, do this with a thick grip. Alternate sides each set.

14 One-leg anterior reach
Time **30 seconds**

WHY DO IT
- It's a classic mobility move that also tests your balance.

HOW TO DO IT
- Stand on one leg and raise the opposite hand. Bend at the hips and touch your knees with your raised hand.
- Don't let your rear leg move behind your standing leg.

15 Reverse cable woodchop
Time **30 seconds**

WHY DO IT
- It builds power for explosive takedowns.

HOW TO DO IT
- Stand with your feet slightly wider than shoulder-width apart, holding a cable attachment in both hands.
- Chop across your body from low to high. For an extra challenge, do this with a thick grip. Alternate sides each set.

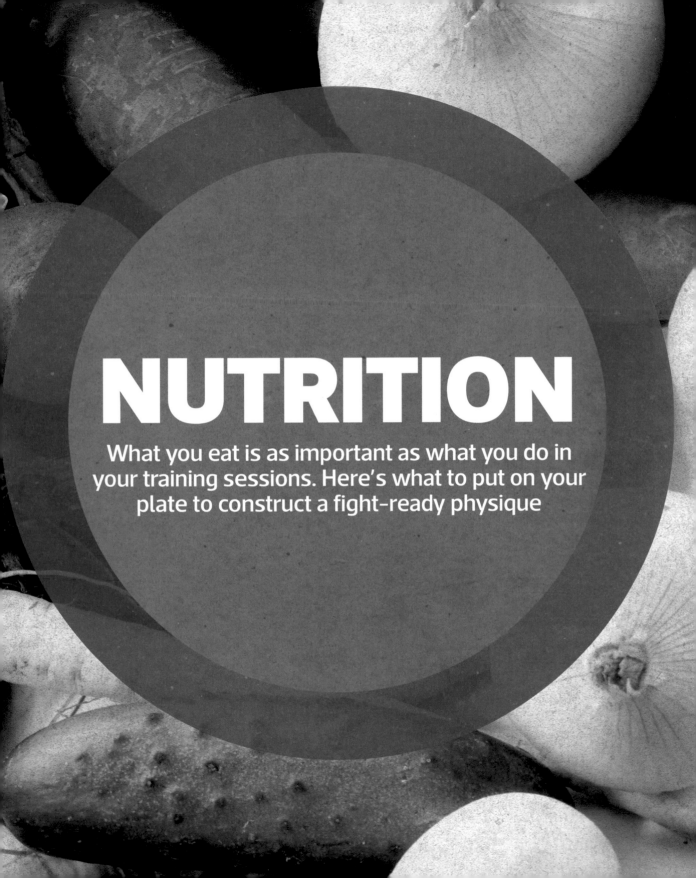

NUTRITION

What you eat is as important as what you do in your training sessions. Here's what to put on your plate to construct a fight-ready physique

FIGHT FUEL

Smart nutrition can make all the difference if you want to get fit to fight

Any modern fighter's goal is to be as strong and fit as possible within his weight class, and that process starts in the kitchen, not the cage. Eating properly will fuel your training sessions, help you feel alert and energised during sparring, provide the building blocks of muscle and give you the best possible strength-to-weight ratio. And even if you've got no intention of stepping on a scale with your shirt off in front of a riled-up crowd, paying attention to your plate will get you lean, ripped and looking like a fighter. Here are the rules to follow.

1 DRINK LOTS OF WATER
When you train you sweat a lot, and you need to need to replace that fluid with water. The trick is to ensure that you hydrate yourself before you get thirsty, not afterwards. Dehydration has an impact on your performance in the gym and the ring – studies estimate that 5% dehydration can lead to a 30% drop in work capacity – and can affect the way your body stores fat and repairs muscle owing to poor organ function. Carry a water bottle around with you all day, sipping from it every few minutes. Over the course of a day you should aim to take in about three litres of water in total – more if you are training intensely.

2 EAT YOUR GREENS
There's no such thing as too much veg, especially if you're talking about vegetables grown above ground. Cruciferous vegetables such as broccoli, kale, cabbage and cauliflower are ideal, and dark, leafy greens such as spinach and rocket are also excellent choices. Regardless of what else you're eating, your plate should be about half-full of vegetables at every meal. Fruit is also good for you, but its high fructose content means it's conducive to the body storing fat so limit yourself to two or three portions a day.

3 PACK IN THE PROTEIN
Protein is one of the most important components of the diet – it's crucial to building muscle, keeps you full, helps tissue repair and the immune system, and provides you with energy. So what's the right amount? Estimates from all the way from one to four grams per kilo of bodyweight, per day, but most nutritionists agree that two grams is the minimum for a hard-training athlete. Aim to eat a wide variety of protein foods to get the full range of muscle-building amino acids: lean meat, fish, eggs and dairy produce are all excellent sources of protein, while lower-quality protein can also be found in nuts, seeds and beans. Include a fist-sized portion in every meal. ▶

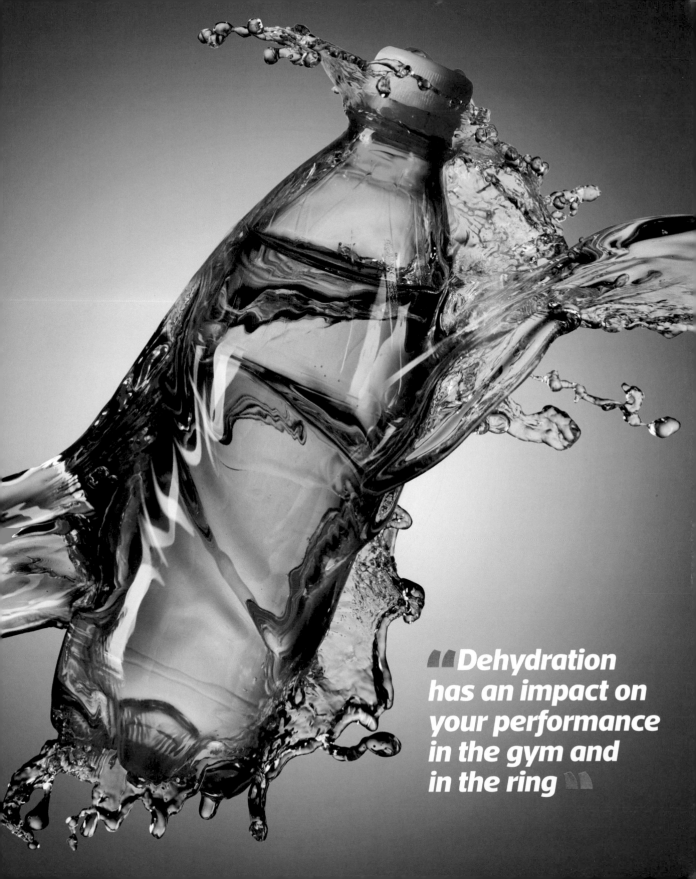

"Dehydration has an impact on your performance in the gym and in the ring"

4 DON'T AVOID FATS

Fats are not all bad. The ones to avoid at all times are trans fats, while some studies suggest that saturated fat intake should be kept low. This means skipping cakes, biscuits and margarine and cutting back on red meats and cheese. The fats you need are monounsaturates and polyunsaturates, found in olive oil, nuts, seeds and oily fish such as salmon and mackerel. These include omega 3 and omega 6 fatty acids, which have been proven to aid strength and aerobic training, protect the body from injuries and help it recover from training wear and tear.

5 ...OR CARBS

When you're trying to lose fat it's sensible to limit your consumption of carbs, especially those from bread, pasta, potatoes and all forms of sugary snacks. But when you're training hard you need the quick-release energy that carbs provide to keep your energy levels high and your muscles fuelled to react quickly and powerfully. Stick to brown rice, sweet potatoes and plenty of vegetables for most of the day, but you can have bread or white rice before training so that you're firing on all cylinders.

6 FREE RANGE IS BETTER

Most experts agree that free-range meat and fish is better for your body. Free-range chickens have a more varied diet and get a lot more exercise so they develop more muscle, which means their meat tends to contain more zinc, vitamins B, A and K, amino acids, iron, selenium, phosphorus and zinc. Farm-raised salmon have also been found to contain more carcinogens than their wild brethren, thanks to cramped conditions and poor-quality feed, while grass-fed beef tends to have higher levels of conjugated linoleic acid and omega 3s than the kind fed on grain and beef tallow. Ultimately, free-range meat is so nutritionally dissimilar to cage-reared that it's basically different food.

7 EAT AT THE RIGHT TIMES

When you're training hard, eat about an hour or two before your workouts, and again immediately afterwards. Your snacks should include both carbs and protein to help restore glycogen levels in your muscles and repair muscle tissue. A perfect post-workout snack might be a bagel with cream cheese, or a tuna and pasta salad. For the rest of the day, eat small meals at regular intervals of two or three hours, and aim to have protein with every meal. This way you keep your glycogen levels topped up and prevent your body from breaking down the proteins that you need for rebuilding muscle.

8 STAY NATURAL

The simplest rule when deciding what to eat: keep it natural. Processed foods – biscuits, cakes, ready meals, fizzy drinks, crisps – tend to be high in calories but low in essential nutrients, so they are poor at fuelling workouts and rebuilding muscle but good at making you fat and sapping your energy. Avoid things containing preservatives that you can't spell or ingredients you wouldn't keep in the kitchen. Eat things that will rot eventually, so that you know they're fresh. As a general rule, if it grows in the ground or used to have a face, it's fine; if it comes in a packet, be wary. ▶

BIGGER, STRONGER, FASTER

Lots of supplements promise miraculous results –
these are the ones that most benefit your training

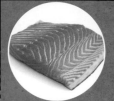

VITAMIN D Unless you eat mounds of wild-caught oily fish or get an unusual amount of sunlight exposure, it's likely that you'd benefit from more vitamin D. Between 25 and 100mcg a day is ideal, and you can take it via gel caps or oral spray.

PROTEIN Don't look on protein shakes as a substitute for animal protein; do use them to up your intake. Use a high-quality fast-acting whey protein shake to repair muscles after training and either whey or slow-release casein at other times throughout the day.

FISH OIL This has a host of benefits, from reducing training-related inflammation and stress to increased focus and fat-burning benefits. Unless your diet already includes a lot of oily fish, aim to supplement with 1–2g of high-quality fish oil per day.

BCAAs Branched-chain amino acid supplements contain valine, leucine and isoleucine, considered 'essential' amino acids because they need to be present in your diet. They're thought to prevent muscle breakdown during intense resistance exercise.

CREATINE This compound is made naturally in the body, but is can also be found in meat and fish or taken as a supplement. It helps produce energy for brief periods of all-out effort with short recovery phases. It's thought the optimum amount is around 3g a day.

ANTIOXIDANTS Antioxidant supplements contain differing amounts of nutrients and plant extracts, including betacarotene, vitamins C and E, zinc, copper and magnesium. They benefit your general health and can also help you recover from sports training.

"Use a fast-acting whey protein shake to repair muscles after training"